CU00650170

A FAMILY AFFAIR

Also by Brigit Barlow

Books
Devil Fish, Chatto & Windus

Short Stories
BBC, *Evening News, Look Now, Womans Way (Eve)*

Articles
Gardening *The Gardener*, Children *Nursing Mirror*, The Business Man *The Times*, Bird Watching *Sunday Telegraph*

Play
Russia and Modern Music

A FAMILY AFFAIR

BRIGIT BARLOW

The Book Guild Ltd
Sussex, England

To E.B., From B.B.
In loving Memory of N.B.

'I am a weathervane of image and memory now.'
Ruth Padel
Siege.

The Book Guild Limited
Temple House
25 High Street
Lewes, Sussex

First published 1990
© Brigit Barlow 1990

Set in Baskerville

Typesetting by Book Economy Services
Burgess Hill

Printed in Great Britain by
Antony Rowe Ltd
Chippenham

British Library Cataloguing in Publication Data
Barlow, Brigit *1928–*
    A family affair.
    1. Fiction in English. Barlow, Brigit *1928–*
    I. Title
    823'914

ISBN 0 86332 462 2

Contents

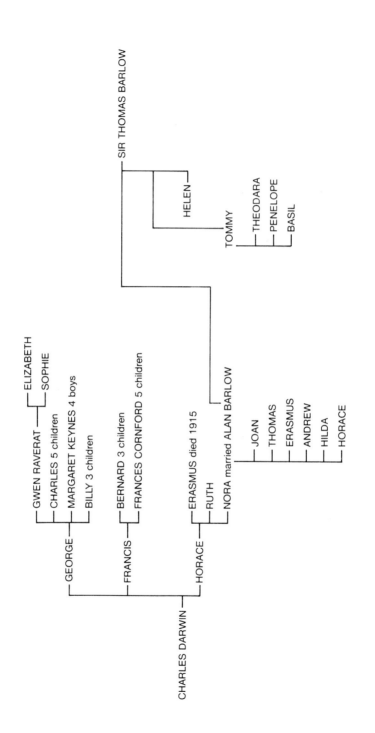

CHARLES DARWIN

GEORGE
— GWEN RAVERAT — ELIZABETH
— SOPHIE
— CHARLES 5 children
— MARGARET KEYNES 4 boys
— BILLY 3 children

FRANCIS
— BERNARD 3 children
— FRANCES CORNFORD 5 children

HORACE
— ERASMUS died 1915
— RUTH
— NORA married ALAN BARLOW

SIR THOMAS BARLOW
— HELEN
— TOMMY
— THEODARA
— PENELOPE
— BASIL

— JOAN
— THOMAS
— ERASMUS
— ANDREW
— HILDA
— HORACE

1

'Such a pale, sickly, little girl,' that was how Nora Barlow always began whenever she recalled our first meeting at a fancy dress party given by her father-in-law for his grand-children.. 'I remember you quite clearly, you were dressed as a fairy.'

If I had contradicted her and said, 'No, Nora, I was dressed as a snowflake,' that would have been historically correct but Nora was a Darwin. No Darwin would ever see any connection between me, a pallid nine-year old in layers of net, and that natural phenomenon, a snowflake.

'You were all in white, looking dreadfully chilly, poor child.' The unflattering description continued until the mention of her son.

'Erasmus was dressed as a mechanic,' I said, 'with grease on his face.

'Yes, in dirty blue overalls.'

Dirty blue and snowy white, yet there was no attraction of opposites, not a hint that one day Erasmus and I would be husband and wife.

The arrival of Sir Thomas Barlow's invitation to the fancy dress party interrupted my mother's writing, and she emerged from her study to discuss with my sister and me what costumes we were to wear. I see her now, standing in the doorway with the card in her hand, as though it was yesterday, yet it was more than half a century ago.

Other details too are crystal clear.

The view through the french windows of a Christmas tree, lying defrocked and prostrate on the lawn waiting to complete the last lap of its journey to the rubbish heap, and the state of the drawing room untidier than usual after a scarf dance. Miss Sayer, had gone off in a huff when we laughed at her imitating Isadora Duncan. She told us to pick up the scarves. We refused, and they remain on the floor of my memory.

Before we went to school, Miss Sayer had been our governess. She now served as a kind of bodyguard for my parents, to protect them from us so that they could write undisturbed. Mills, the Barlow's chauffeur, had upset my mother by delivering the invitation with a hefty knock on the door. She couldn't continue writing her story with the two words 'fancy dress' niggling her mind. She must get the question of our costumes settled as quickly as possible. Gill would be amenable to any suggestion but she wasn't so sure about me.

'Gill, you can squeeze into your grandmother's ball dress and with your hair in ringlets you'll look lovely. Biddy. . .' she paused and suppressed a sigh, 'you had better be a gipsy, but something will have to be done to give you a swarthy tan.' Gill was delighted. I scowled.

'I want to be a snowflake,' I said, 'and I want to wear white.'

I loved white and had once been accused of lacking imagination when I drew a mountain range with a white crayon on a white sheet of paper. My mother suggested enlivening my picture with a few fir trees and skiers, but I stubbornly refused, just as I refused now to be a gypsy when she talked about a spotted bandanna and curtain rings.

'You're making a mistake,' she said, and escaped to her world of romantic fiction which supplemented the income from my father's more serious writing. We were left to get on with our Christmas thank-you letters to aunts in Ireland whom we'd never met.

My parents gave all their spare time to politics. My father wrote my mother's speeches which she rehearsed in front of us when we were in bed. She met Sir Thomas Barlow at political meetings in Wendover. They sat on the platform together and applauded what each other said. Because he voted Liberal it was all right for us to accept an invitation to his house. We took as a matter of course the political prejudice which governed our social contacts. The families with whom we mixed were all easy-going, hospitable and had the same standards as ourselves, only later I felt a retrospective deprivation on discovering that many families with similar qualities actually voted – dare I write it? – Conservative.

Preparation for the party produced unforeseen tensions

when my sister's hair refused to curl because of an attack of
the fidgets and I turned so pale with apprehension that my
face almost matched my snowflake costume. However, we
were ready on time and sat in our velvet cloaks on either side
of Miss Sayer in the taxi. We were used to being entertained in
big houses but as soon as we were out of Wendover it became
obvious that this was something on a different scale. A whole
fleet of cars turned up the drive, which seemed to go on
forever. Berberis hedges gave way to dripping beeches. We
passed a lodge with a neat little front garden, a scatter of farm
buildings, and then the first sight of Boswells. Every window
was ablaze with light. And there were so many windows. I
had to be dragged from the taxi and pushed through the
front door into a large hall filled with a swirling mass of
children whose fancy dress added to the illusion that this was
a dream, a bad dream. We shed our cloaks, Miss Sayer disappeared, and in admiration and dismay I watched my sister
make a bee-line for a slide at the far end of the hall. Soon she
was enjoying herself and her dress, the precious heirloom,
was reduced to shreds as she slid down the slide laughing and
talking to the other children. Pip, Squeak and Wilfred the
favourite fancy dress costumes of the time all quickly became
her friends.

I stood as close to the fire as possible until a gong boomed
and a queue formed to shake hands with a tubby, little man
like a garden gnome with red cheeks and white beard, whom
I assumed correctly to be our host, Sir Thomas Barlow.

'Very nice, my dear, very nice.' He said the same thing
about each child's costume, and having received my quota of
praise I entered the dining-room, where angry William
Morris wallpaper fought with the furious Morris curtains
hanging in heavy folds over the windows, but failing to keep
out the draught. Grateful for a blazing log fire, unlike the
sulky one in the hall, that now warmed my back, I sat next to
my sister at a long table, nibbling slowly through a bridge roll
spread with fishy paste; not daring to ask for a glass of milk I
found myself given a cup of pale grey tea and having to
manoeuvre silver tongs round sugar lumps while a parlour-
maid bent double to hold the bowl within my reach.

Not being engaged in any conversation I was able to sort
out the Barlow grandchildren from the other guests. They

called a large bustly woman with untidy gingery hair, blue
eyes and a cheerful smile 'Aunt Helen', and the smaller,
more demure one in a fair isle jersey and tweed skirt
'Mama'.

Miss Barlow had great authority with her nephews and
nieces. As soon as tea was over she announced that there was
going to be a game in the school room, and Thomas was told
to do this, Erasmus that, Horace, Hilda, Andrew and Joan
were all given jobs and none of them argued or answered
back.

The game was called 'clumps'. When I heard there were
going to be teams my fear of being picked last made it
impossible to attend to the complicated rules. Although my
sister badgered the team leader into choosing me early on I
still had to suffer the humiliation of not knowing what to do
when everyone started running to and fro, screaming with
happy laughter.

Such was the volume of noise that Mrs Barlow, after whispered consultation with her sister-in-law, called a halt to the
game and suggested that we should come into the drawing
room and calm down by listening to some music. She be-
ckoned me over to sit next to her, and there close to the fire I
watched the dancing sparks in the soot at the back of the
chimney while Miss Barlow sang songs, accompanying herself on the piano.

Surely the party must be over soon, then we could go home
and I would tell my mother how much I had enjoyed being a
snowflake. The singing stopped, and I was ready on my feet,
eager to find my cloak and escape into the dark, whether the
taxi was there or not, when Miss Barlow ordered us all to stay
where we were.

'I am going to tell you a story,' she said, and motioned to
Thomas to switch off the lights. Nothing now but the faint
glow of the fire and the shuffle of restless feet. Some of the
children let out suitable squeaks as Miss Barlow's story slowly
unfurled; one self-appointed cheer-leader whipped up a little
enthusiasm by emitting sporadic gasps of 'ooh' and 'ah', but I
stubbornly refused to react. The climax came when a white-
clad figure with glowing eyes appeared from behind the
Morris curtains. How feeble, it was so obviously Erasmus
covered in a sheet and holding two torches in front of his

eyes. My house was *officially* haunted and a *real* ghost made the stairs creak outside the nursery door while my brother told blood-curdling tales far into the night. With the warm glow of superiority I began rather late in the day to enjoy myself. That fancy dress party marked the end of an era. Shortly afterwards, I'm not sure exactly when, the world of governesses, taxis and maids calling me 'Miss Biddy' came to an end. And it ended with my mother making the announcement that we were now poor. One day we were well off and the next day we weren't. She came into the nursery, a long room with oak beams and iron bedsteads to break the news to us. She looked just the same as she always did, with a smile stretched over a worried face. She explained that from now on there would not be chocolate biscuits for tea and we would have to make our own beds. My vocabulary increased – creditors, debts, and bankruptcy now became familiar words. The Depression had caught my father unawares. He had run up a few debts assuming he could settle them when his next story sold, but the stories did not sell. The markets had collapsed – where there had been four magazines there was now only one, or worse still, none. He went on writing, dictating thousands and thousands of words each day to his secretary in his study.

We had to be educated and we had to have the best education the neighbourhood could offer – Berkhamstead High School rather than Aylesbury Grammar,which meant a car, coach and train journey each day instead of a simple five mile ride in a bus which stopped outside our front door. He was against boarding schools on principle and would never have sent us away to school even if he could have afforded it, but that did not stop him from poring over Whittaker's Almanac and working out what parents who did not share his principles had to pay for their children's education. When we got to know the Barlows better and he discovered Thomas was at Winchester, Erasmus at Marlborough and Andrew at Eastbourne College he exclaimed, 'How does anyone find the money to pay such fees?' The answer of course was a private income – words not part of my vocabulary yet.

In nineteen–thirty Sir Thomas Barlow and his daughter, Helen, retired to their London house in Wimpole Street and Alan, being the elder son, moved into Boswells with Nora and their six children. It was a wrench for Nora to leave the beautiful old house in Chesham Bois which was suitably named The Warren. She must have gone to Boswells from a sense of duty, grieving for the garden she had created and resenting the professional landscaping of the one to which she now had to adapt. She disliked the neo-Elizabethan facade of Boswells and the flamboyant William Morris decor inside was far too overwhelming for her modest taste. She covered the dining-room walls with blue-grey distemper, blocked in the fireplace and built a stand to display Alan's Tang horse in a glass case, but there she stopped. She never did anything more except complain quite openly about Boswell's basic faults, which she couldn't hope to alter. The house was too big. It faced the wrong way. The kitchen got more sun than any of the other rooms. Although there was always Bean, the chauffeur, to swoop up the gravel drive to the front door she objected to the garage being so far away.

'Such a pretentious piece of design,' she said, a veiled criticism of her father-in-law, perhaps, who had built the place in 1910.

Nora liked things simple and what we offered in our house was exactly that, the slump not having curbed our easy-going hospitality although standards had necessarily dropped. A last minute extra person for supper just meant laying an extra place and perhaps the family holding back. A guest might only be offered poached egg on toast with stewed plums to follow, but lively conversation round the table always made up for any lack of haute cuisine – my brothers saw to that.

My parents always presided over the meals, my mother serving the simple food with tarnished, crested silver and my father pouring dilute lemonade into chipped Waterford glasses. Once the meal was over they disappeared, leaving us to entertain our friends. There was no television set to turn on; instead the gramophone came to our rescue. Records had to be changed every few minutes and inserting a needle with a hand shaking from social pressure could take a long time. We often rolled up the carpets and danced to well-worn records, or rehearsed a play which never got very far because of arguments over who should have the leading part. Mostly we just sat around and talked in front of a blazing fire, provided of course there was enough coal to blaze and the cheque for last month's delivery had been met.

Our friends drifted into the house often not bothering to knock at the front door. We never achieved such easy terms with them; and the entertainment they offered, although less frequent, was always better organised. Our closest friends, geographically speaking, were the Wise family. They lived a couple of hundred yards away in a house as old and rambling as our own. Frank Wise, we all knew, would be Prime Minister *if* the Independent Labour Party ever got into power, and although that seemed unlikely the remote possibility gave him prestige. He always wore a white polo-neck sweater which showed off his black hair and dark eyes. Charades dominated their parties which Frank threw himself into with great gusto, helping the girls to dress up and cracking jokes I couldn't understand but left me feeling uneasy.

The Addison family was comfortingly hard up. Their house looked as shabby as ours. Dr Addison was a Labour member of parliament and mostly away from home. His wife was always dealing with some crisis of a gynaecological nature, either a birth or a miscarriage, sometimes both at once, so I never saw much of her either. We played croquet on a bumpy lawn in summer and in winter stumbled through rooms to find a crowd under a bed ready to shout 'sardine' at the last person left looking.

The Ewer's parties were the most lavish. Trilby Ewer was the *Daily Herald*'s foreign correspondent, and Monica, his wife, wrote novels. They had a son called Denis, Bink, Jakes – call him by any name and my first impression of him will always be the same – a boy with a deep bass voice wearing very short shorts, sitting on a table in front of his guests, swinging his hairy legs and shouting every few minutes 'Let's have a revolution' while his parents tried in vain to persuade him to join in some innocent game – 'squeak piggy squeak', I think it was.

Both my parents came from Conservative backgrounds. My maternal grandfather was a skeleton in the cupboard. I only discovered by chance he had been Conservative MP for Harrow. My parents thought themselves very broadminded politically. Anyone left of centre was perfectly acceptable to them. An enclave of Socialists lived comfortably housed on

Cobbler's Hill between Great Missenden and Wendover.

Rachel Keeting belonged to this set, only she lived in a railway carriage when not being bohemian in her Bloomsbury flat. She was my mother's best friend; scarcely a day passed without her calling at our house. I never got to know her; she was just someone who came, spent an hour or so talking to my mother in the drawing-room and then went. She had been married to Ben Keeling and was now a widow, lonely and always slightly flushed.

The Barlows living less than two miles away transformed our limited social life into what, by comparison, seemed a social whirl. There were frequent invitations for us to come to Boswells. The mixed hockey matches I remember best.

We assembled early in the afternoon on the verandah, where hockey sticks in varying stages of decrepitude were laid out. The beefier children rushed to grab the best stick and I always hung back, praying that if I waited long enough there would not be enough sticks to go round and I would escape the ordeal of standing shivering on the pitch, dreading a ball might come in my direction and knock out my front teeth. Frozen cold I consumed chilly orange slices at half time, pretending I was enjoying myself and longing for the whistle to sound so that we could go back into the house.

Then the fun would begin. Murder in the dark. It was worth suffering on the hockey pitch just for this. The Barlow boys – that was how we thought of them – were pleasant, polite and definitely inhibited but once the lights were switched out, they went berserk. A decision had to be made – should I stay in the hall and be safe from the marauding boys or should I advance step by step up the staircase to the landing and join in the squeals (Is that a proper scream or isn't it?) and make contact with the groping hands that were everywhere? With tingling excitement I made the journey to the landing. The comfortable tread of the stairs, the smooth wood of the banister, yes, I can recapture the excitement now.

Unlike my own parents Nora was always present, unobtrusive and in the background, but her influence nevertheless felt. If the high spirits got out of hand she might put in a plea for quiet.

'Why are you always so badly behaved when the Black family come to tea?' she asked. My brothers had been leading

her own children astray. Biscuits with different animals iced
on them had caused unruly mirth. How those Playmate biscuits could produce such a response it is difficult to imagine,
but my brothers had the knack. They could make fun of
anything.

I was a little in awe of Nora. Unlike my mother she never
expressed her thoughts and feelings freely and I mistook this
reticence for disapproval, particularly if I had a guilty conscience. I felt immensely guilty when she discovered Andrew
and me sitting in front of the school-room fire listening to
Beethoven's Fifth Symphony on the gramophone when I
should have been out on the cold hockey pitch. Suffering the
indignity of my first period I had managed to escape from the
verandah gathering to Andrew who, recovering from polio,
was unable to join the other children in the fresh air. I can
hardly believe Nora was anything but delighted at finding her
son with company, but because she didn't say anything to that
effect I assumed she must be annoyed.

It took a long association with the Barlows, Erasmus in particular, whose middle name should have been 'Control'
rather than 'Darwin', for me to realise that lack of emotional
display did not necessarily mean absence of emotion. In my
family we flung our emotions around the place and regularly
once a week my father lost his temper with the Sunday joint,
which developed a will of its own as soon as he began to carve.
He swore and spluttered abuse as he slashed away with a
knife. What was normal behaviour in my home was unthink-
able at Boswells and as soon as I became aware of the difference I began to dread doing something wrong.

After a hockey match Nora found me on the verandah
cleaning mud off my shoes. I was dressed for the party, not the
pitch, and Nora's opening comment, 'You're frozen cold,'
sounded like a rebuke.

'I'm warm, really I am,' I said, 'it's just that my shoes are
dirty.' Inadequate shoes. Why wasn't I wearing wellingtons or
boots like everyone else? I knew that was what she must be
thinking although all she said was,

'Your feet must be wet. You'd better come upstairs and
change. I'll lend you a pair of my stockings.'

I followed her up to her bedroom and stood awkwardly in
the bay window, looking out at the flowery valley while she

rummaged in her drawer, although 'rummage' is the wrong word because most likely everything in that drawer was tidy. I smelled in that room for the first time the distinctive smell that all Darwin houses carry. It is not unpleasant. It is a mixture of furniture polish, pot-pourri and some special ingredient which only Darwins have, the missing link, which I can't name.

'There now,' said Nora, 'I think this pair will do.' She left me alone with my frozen fingers fumbling at suspenders. The room was bitterly cold. The stockings were in a neat bundle with the tops turned over, and as I unrolled them I realised that they were made of heavy silk, not like the lisle ones I had taken off. On they went, a bit big perhaps, but what a joy to wear until I noticed that one had a ladder, a great, long ladder from the knee to the toe. What should I do? Downstairs a relentless gong was booming everyone into tea. Tempted to put the stockings back in the drawer and help myself to a less incriminating pair I undid my suspenders, then fearing I might be caught in the act, I put the stockings on again, willing the ladder to have disappeared, but it was still there, if anything more conspicuous than before. I felt like a criminal in the bitterly cold room with that funny Darwin smell and everyone laughing downstairs in the hall. I had been inadequately shod, not a serious crime, but a devastating one if it led to me ruining a pair of best silk stockings. I felt miserable during tea and afterwards, finding Nora on her own, confessed the truth.

'I'm terribly sorry,' I stammered, 'but the stockings you lent me have a huge ladder in them.' I twisted my leg round for her to see. Her face softened. She smiled and then to my surprise she laughed.

'How terribly embarrassing for you,' she exclaimed. 'I'm so sorry. What a silly thing for me to have done. I can imagine exactly how you felt.' My eyes filled with tears at her kindness, and she seeing those tears rested her hand on mine for a moment. That small incident was a big event.

These hockey matches which played an important part in our early adolescence were organised by Nora. She saw that everything was ready in advance, from the referee's whistle to a cow-pat free pitch. She supervised the tea for twenty-two or more and then launched us into some game – which for me justified the afternoon's ordeal in the cold. While we enjoyed ourselves I like to think that Nora put her feet up and relaxed; but that would have been contrary to her nature and most likely she used the valuable time sitting at her bureau, editing scientific papers or writing one of those letters which at their most affectionate began 'My Dear', and ended with 'Love N.'

In the Easter holidays Nora sometimes substituted a chalk chase for the hockey match as a means of getting her family out in the fresh air for exercise. Usually the same crowd of young people turned up – the Wises, the Addisons, Denis Ewer and a cousin or two. The Barlows had an endless supply of cousins.

Those who had been the most active on the hockey pitch opted now to be 'hares'. They ran ahead, leaving a trail of chalk arrows across the countryside to be followed by the 'hounds', whose aim was to catch them up before they reached their base. It was a modified form of the lake hunt, which the older generation of Barlows and Darwins had enjoyed. But we lacked their energy, and unless a 'hound' particularly liked a 'hare', 'keen on' we called it then, 'fancied' now, there was no hot pursuit, just dawdling along and breaking into an occasional sprint if someone thought they spotted the 'hares' not too far ahead.

On one memorable occasion Erasmus decided to dispense with the energetic part of the afternoon. He overheard Nora on the phone arranging for us to have tea at the Black Horse in Scrub Wood. Realising this was to be our destination he drove straight there, squeezing thirteen 'hounds' into the open Sunbeam, some sitting on knees while others perched on the rolled-up hood. The 'hares' didn't know we were not following closely on their tracks until they arrived panting, at the pub, rather annoyed to find us round the table, enjoying our tea.

And Nora didn't know Erasmus had borrowed the car until Keane, who lived in the lodge, reported what he had seen while peering between the net curtains of his window. Nora, although she disliked this red-faced bailiff of her father-in-law, felt obliged to satisfy his demand for punishment. The reproof was typically mild. Erasmus' behaviour had been a little irresponsible, since he had only recently learned to drive and it might have been most inconvenient to have found the car missing from the garage when she needed it, so another time would ye please let her know. . . .

In summer we had supper picnics on the Round Hill behind Boswells. They were innocent get-togethers. No-one ever strayed from the bonfire and a kiss on the cheek would warrant an entry in my diary followed by a couple of exclamation marks. Next morning Keane always went up to search for evidence of our goings on. His imagination matched his florid complexion, and patches of flattened grass, flattened by the rabbits, perhaps, certainly not by us, were proof of what we had been doing. His fictitious accounts of our behaviour received a negative response from Nora, and I only hope he found a better audience in the servants' hall beyond the green baize door.

Informers were rife in those days. A hostess, often with an axe to grind, would feel it her social duty to let a mother know if her child had not behaved properly. The phrase 'I'm sure you'd want to know' was of course completely untrue. No mother wanted to know about her child's misbehaviour. I was resigned to a lecture the next day if the night before if I had enjoyed myself which all too soon came to mean one thing only –flirting.

'Anything in trousers,' my mother exclaimed in despair, 'I'm sure you'll flirt with the undertaker who measures you for your coffin.'

Such remonstrations went in one ear and out the other, just as well perhaps, because eventually she was driven to try more drastic methods to break this bad habit of mine by giving a graphic description of the physiological changes that took place in a male when I began giving what she termed 'the glad eye'.

These morning after the night before rows took place in my mother's bedroom. On one occasion at least Teedie got into trouble too. He had been seen kissing Margaret Wise at a party in our house. She was a beautiful girl, demure, hair parted down the middle, destined to be a clergyman's wife and definitely not my brother's type – hence if he kissed her he must be drunk and that was as bad as flirting. There was very little drink in our house. In more prosperous days there had been a beer barrel in the cellar, and my father used to send me there to re-fill his tankard, but that disappeared overnight along with the chocolate biscuits. Cider cup, very dilute, was the only alcoholic beverage we could offer our friends, and I doubt if Teedie could have got drunk on that!

Nora was more broad-minded about flirting than my mother was. She told me as though it was amusing and rather daring, that she and her Darwin cousins, Frances and Gwen, had one day decided to FLIRT. I have no idea how they set about it, or on whom they practised their talents but from what she told me they seemed to lack dedication and the whole exercise turned out to be an anti-climax, like a scientific experiment with a negative result.

When my brothers became interested in the radio, or wireless as it was called then, they rigged up their own broadcasting system which, by a lengthy wire from the dining-room, enabled them to shout abuse at anyone sitting in the drawing-room. Soon the random ravings grew into well delivered speeches, and before long my father wrote a short play, which needed an appreciative audience. The Barlows were invited and once they had accepted, rehearsals began. Although it was not necessary to learn lines, one had to come in promptly on cue, and that required a certain skill. Tempers became frayed, bad language fouled my father's script, and there was an atmosphere of first night nerves when we grouped ourselves around the microphone. Any swear word we let slip would be relayed through the loud speaker to the Barlows sitting in the drawing-room.

The Barlows clapped enthusiastically when it was all over, and once the congratulations had died down Nora, with a deprecating smile, announced,

'We have prepared something for you. It's only a sketch.' We were dumbfounded. Usually friends who came to our house sat around waiting to be entertained by us, and here was a family actually offering something for our amusement without being asked.

The sketch was a take-off of Wendover life, and began with an incomprehensible gabble, which was easily recognisable as the tiresome chatter of a garrulous lady we all dreaded meeting in the High Street. Helpless with laughter, we rolled around on the sofa as each new character was introduced. The sound effects were used to best advantage on a visit to a farm, especially when a pack of cards dropped on a table sounded exactly like a cow doing a very sloppy cow-pat.

Music was a common ground, and like all common ground, offered opportunity for dissent. We worshipped Beethoven, whom the Barlows considered very emotional, a derogatory term. I disliked Mozart until an unforgettable performance of *Eine Kleine Nacht Musik* played by the Barlow family in our house. Nora conducted this amateur orchestra although she had never held a baton before in her life. They were together for the first bar and the last chord; what happened in between was a tuneful, scratchy affair that left me spellbound. A family making music, each child with a different instrument, was an impressive sight, whatever the sound. And in return, my father and I played a duet, perhaps? Maybe Gill recited one of her poems? I don't know. All I remember is Nora's straight back as she stood there with baton raised, willing her children to come in on time.

One Saturday night at Boswells, just as the family sat down to dinner and Alan, in his velvet smoking jacket, was carving the roast chicken, with a parlour maid passing round the plates, the whole house was plunged into darkness. A scuffle of footsteps; a vase, not a celadon, but something shoddy and cheap, vanished from the schoolroom mantlepiece. Nora, ready for such an emergency with torch and whistle at hand, quickly organised a search party to go into the garden. High up a tree I listened to her rattling out orders.

'Erasmus, over to the croquet lawn; Hilda, to the front door; Horace and Joan, you stay on the verandah and Thomas, look in the bushes – only take care not to step on the cyclamen.

This was all part of a game inspired by –Tam's crazy genius. We two families planned that between certain hours we would try to break into each others' houses and steal a specified object from a pre-arranged place. Although Nora approved of the game and played an important part in it, dashing around in the dark, like an air-raid warden, she can't really have been pleased with Tam posing as the electricity man. He turned off the power at source, disrupting the dinner, and upsetting the maid who let him in at the back door, believing he had come to read the meter.

We spent a jittery evening waiting for the Barlows to burgle our house. By ten o'clock nothing had happened. It would be difficult for them to equal our brilliant coup, and after another hour had passed we decided they must have given up. Disappointed that the game had had such an unsatisfactory end, I went upstairs, only to find the game was still very much in progress. Behind my bedroom door, pressed against the wall, was as young man, a German Jew, the first of many befriended by the Barlows. I had never seen him before; I never saw him again, but I see him now – his curly brown hair, and white plimsolls. His astonished expression could have been due to partaking in such an extraordinary game or the sight of me in my nightdress.

When Nora invited me to stay with them at their sea-side cottage in Norfolk I wouldn't believe my luck, until she made it clear, with her usual tact, that the journey would not involve my parents in any expense as we would be travelling there by car.

'Bean will drive us,' she explained, 'he will go on to stay with relatives in Cromer.' Everything beautifully arranged down to the last detail.

I had not been to the sea at any other time than the summer when my parents, incapable of planning ahead, rented what was left on the market at the last minute; my father could never afford not to work, so the house had to be big enough to accommodate the family plus a few hangers-on, and his secretary with the typewriter.

Here I was in April, yes April, without any hassle, peacefully driving through the flat countryside which seemed to me more beautiful than any other place I'd seen before. We stopped for a picnic and had our lunch in a coppice near the road. Bean had the same sandwiches as we had but he ate them standing a few yards away from where we sat on a tree trunk. The April sun was almost hot, the wind was sharp. At Brandon Nora bought a large pork pie from the butcher's shop, which had been ordered in advance. 'That will save cooking,' she said, and her voice suddenly lifted, as though she'd been freed from a prison.

Hillside was a great contrast to Boswells. Nothing pretentious about this flint-faced cottage with a nose of a door in the middle and windows like eyes on either side. Nora revelled in the simplicity. She seemed positively proud of the earth closet

outside the back door and the inadequate supply of hot water
that meant baths had to be rationed. The meter needed constant feeding with shillings that she enjoyed hoarding in her
purse. When she drew the tattered curtains and they didn't
quite meet, she gave another tug and said, 'That will do,' an
expression of hers I was to get to know quite well.

During the day we often lit fires on the beach from
driftwood, and cooked sausages which, either burnt or
slightly raw, were always a smoky delight. We ate doughnuts
from the bakery in Sheringham and for supper Nora opened
tins – sardines, pilchards, corned beef, ham – 'That will do,'
she said, arranging whatever it was on a plate.

The washing-up was done by the kitchen maid who had
gone ahead to prepare the house for us. Born and bred in
Norfolk she had a typically dumpling face. I never knew her
name. She was nameless and every evening practically invis-
ible, too, when she sat among the hanging coats in the boiler
room reading a book while we played noisy games in
another room.

At night I listened to a train puffing along the single track
line. We were near enough to the sea to hear the waves breaking on the beach when the wind got up. I was happy with the
Barlows, far happier than I usually was staying away from
home. Week-ends with school friends in Watford and Hemel
Hempstead were often drear experiences that could only be
endured by ticking off the hours until the moment came to say
'Goodbye and thank you for the lovely time.'

On an outing to Sheringham Nora and Joan took me to a
shop in a back street which sold a vast range of things under
the heading of fisherman's gear. There Nora bought me a
navy blue jersey smelling faintly of oil, very thick, very warm,
with a cable stitch yoke and a high neck, the same jersey that
her children wore. I now felt accepted, as though wearing the
right uniform made me one of them. Next day I was disillusioned. After distributing binoculars among the family
Nora asked me if I liked birds.

'I love birds,' I replied, thinking of the injured ones
wrapped in warm flannel that I helped my mother nurse back
to health with sips of whisky in front of the fire. How different
was the Barlows' love of birds. They suffered a biting East
wind on an exposed bank above a dyke in order to call some

bird by the right name. There was a lot of shushing and standing around and peering at little specks on the marshes which
disappeared as soon as I focused my binoculars on them. A
bittern booming? Yes, it really was a bittern booming. Sssh
. . . there it goes again and look over there, to the right above
the rushes, something with a spotted breast . . . could it be a
reed warbler or was it. . . ? As I couldn't share their
enthusiasm I wanted to ridicule it, to giggle at the humourless
way they talked about the spotted breast; I wanted to invent
some high-falutin' name for a bird that didn't exist – a greater
green backed yellow spotted flap-jack came to mind but I
decided against it, remained quiet, and when we got back to
Hillside I felt the urge to write home.

Hillside
West Runton

Darling Mummy, Daddy, Tam, Teedie and Gill,
We arrived here safely, stopping for a picnic on the way.
Yesterday we walked to Cromer and BACK. On our return
we ran into a most awful thunderstorm and with thunder-
claps roaring above our heads and hail beating relentlessly
against our faces we made our way across the open and
unprotected golf links. We were utterly drenched by the
time we got home.
Horace is an excellent companion. We both went 'Ludo'
mad yesterday. It is an excellent game. Horace does all the
swearing which is lucky. On Friday evening *Erasmus*,
Andrew and Mr Barlow arrived and the four of us played
'Ludo' until eleven o'clock and then we played a gambling
game with dice. I won.
I am enjoying myself. I feel wonderfully fit. Erasmus is so
like his father. Horace is adorable I have fallen completely.
Erasmus will fight with him. Andrew seems literally years
older than all of us. I am getting on well with Joan. Well I
must stop now as Horace is making polite hints about
Ludo.
Much love to all,
Biddy
PS Did Gill go to the Pacifist meeting? Horace and I read an
account of it in the paper. Erasmus said the *News Chronicle*

was a lousy newspaper and Horace flew at him and said he shouldn't say rude things about a paper Teedie wrote for. I really am enjoying myself.

In his youth Erasmus had a reputation for being quick-tempered, quite fiery, in fact, which bore little resemblance to the Mr Barlow in my letter. Alan was a taciturn man, who, in all the years that I knew him only lost his temper once. And that was on this holiday, when Nora took a leather bound book from the shelf to put under the leg of the dining-room table to stop if from rocking during lunch.

'That is my copy of David Copperfield,' Alan said, quite a long sentence for him.

Nora didn't exactly shrug her shoulders, but she looked as though she wanted to when she replied, 'I know.'

'You shouldn't use a book for that sort of thing,' Alan spluttered.

'Why not?' asked Nora, with a defiant jut of her chin, 'I think it's rather good for Dickens to be put under the table leg for a change.

Alan was furious, but the book remained where it was until lunch was over. I never saw such a display of temper again but there was no reason, at this early stage, for me to know that this was the exception and not the rule, which explains, perhaps, why I wrote home that Erasmus was so like his father.

My other observations need no justification. Horace was adorable and I did get on well with Joan. Not everyone got on well with Joan; some people treated her as though she didn't exist and others became embarrassed whenever she spoke. Speaking for Joan was complicated by a cleft palate and hare lip. Early operations had left her with a 'saucer face' and out of this face there looked beautiful, but agonised eyes when she tried to converse. Although she was the eldest child, she found it difficult to keep up with her younger siblings, and often got left out of games unless Nora was there to make sure she joined in. I admired Joan's industry. Unlike me she never sat around gazing out of windows or dreaming in front of the fire. She was always doing something – copying out music, practicing the 'cello or binding on book jackets that had come adrift. When we were alone together we talked. Many of the opinions she expressed were following the party line, regurgitated

Nora, and it took me many years to find out what the real Joan felt; for the moment she was part of a family who added such fun to my life, that homogeneous mass of Barlows, out of which Erasmus was soon to emerge as the one I loved best.

2

Falling in love coincided with other events during the Christmas holidays which showed, outwardly at any rate, I was growing up. I had by fifteen at last developed a bosom. Unconfined by a bra it bounced around under my jersey which meant I often had my arms folded across my chest. My mother was opposed to her daughters wearing brassieres. I never knew why. Unlike ankle socks and berets a bra couldn't be condemned as a Conservative symbol yet it was black-listed nevertheless.

My mother had many quirks about what we wore. It took a lot of wheedling on my part to persuade her to allow me to have a party dress that went half way down the calf, to the top of the clocks of my stockings to be exact, instead of above the knee.

I wore my new dress to the Wise's dance and behaved with even less decorum than usual. Thomas and Erasmus were there and although I admired Thomas's – 'Manners maketh man', the school motto, had had an effect – it was Erasmus's company I sought. We spent most of the evening together, pairing up for the games and rushing into each other's arms for the last waltz. Next day I felt more than usually moody; nothing was happening, why couldn't the telephone ring or there be a knock at the door?

After the excitement of the night before, life seemed insufferably flat. Exasperated by my sulky face my mother said, 'You were so cheerful yesterday and look at you now. Why can't you keep an even keel?' That was a favourite expression of hers. She always came nautical when my high spirits unaccountably dived into a trough. Tam was told to take me for a walk. Fresh air and exercise would do me good. It must. It was such a grey, bleak, cold, December afternoon.

I trudged along a few paces behind my brother, glad that his bizarre comments rarely needed any reply. Suddenly, through the mist, a group of people appeared coming towards us. The Barlow children, all six of them, were also taking enforced exercise in the fresh air. When they recognised fellow sufferers their martyred expressions lightened. We were invited back to tea by Nora, the children begging us to come, but my brother's string of conflicting excuses made it clear nothing would induce him to accept. He loathed going into other people's houses. We said goodbye and went our separate ways, the Barlows to their house and we to ours, but before we disappeared from sight in the thickening mist I looked back just as Erasmus turned round, we waved to each other and at that moment I knew I was in love. It was the last day of the year, December 31, 1932.

This was something different from the crushes I had had on other boys, whose affections no sooner gained were often discarded. There was nothing to report in my diary, no satisfactory progress from holding hands to kiss on cheek.

Days without Erasmus were days lost. Every party suffered the Robin Adair syndrome if he wasn't there. Hoping to see him I offered to do the shopping but rarely returned with the right goods because my head was on a swivel looking out for the Barlow's Sunbeam, praying Erasmus would be at the wheel. If I did meet him I had no hesitation about cadging a lift to a trumped-up destination and then manufacturing another meeting by leaving something behind in the car which he would be obliged to return at a later, palpitating date. Gloves, scarves, handkerchiefs, all played their part in my little schemes – but to no avail. Erasmus remained the same, charming and friendly and as unattainable as my favourite film star, Romon Navarro, had always been.

My mother told me not to be silly. 'It will be somebody else next week,' she said, exasperated by my behaviour; but when Erasmus went back to school and she found me in tears her tone changed. 'I really believe he has touched your stony little heart,' she exclaimed, and looked concerned on my behalf.

I went off my food, felt dizzy and couldn't do my homework without parental help. My mother having encouraged me to cultivate an interest had to tolerate a petticoat being cut out on the drawing-room table with endless mutterings of 'baste, clip, slip stitch', from me as I tried to follow the paper pattern instructions. The garment, if it were ever finished, although not exactly blacklisted, would fall into the category of unnecessary frippery. She was probably as grateful as I was to the door bell that interrupted this moderately creative activity. Nora came into the drawing room, witnessed the industrious girl bent over the table, visibly approved and issued an invitation for me to go with her and Joan to visit Erasmus at Marlborough the next day. Virtue rewarded, I dispensed with my sewing and began fussing about what to wear. Nora's injunction to wrap up warm was ignored. Next morning for a long journey in an unheated car I put on a summer weight cream skirt and matching shantung blouse. I assured Nora my tweed coat was warmer than it looked. With the three of us, Joan, Nora and myself, snuggled together on the back seat, rugs up to our chins and foot warmers on our feet, we could keep out the cold.

Bean, the chauffeur, drove at a steady pace, far too steady for my liking; I tried to will that solid, navy blue back to put a foot down on the accelerator, break the speed limit, and get me to Marlborough where Erasmus would be waiting, and not expecting me. How would he react? To pass time I suggested playing games; Joan and I killed off several miles with 'I Spy' and scoring letter boxes on the side of the road. Somewhere at the edge of my self-centredness I was aware of Nora's pleasure at the effort I was making with Joan.

When we reached Marlborough Nora said, 'He'll be in the music room, practising his violin,' and with her purposeful walk disappeared into a red brick building, leaving me and Joan outside. Crows cawing, banging doors, muffled scales on a piano produced a grating cacophony as I waited with shivers running up and down my back for Erasmus to appear.

'I suppose he's in the library working,' Nora said on her return. Over to the library we traipsed. My legs felt wobbly. Was it emotion or the long journey that made them feel so weak?

'We had better go to Cotton House and ask where he is,' Nora said. We got back in the car, and drove to the outskirts of the town, up a gravel drive to one of the ugliest houses I had ever seen. The whiff of cabbage cooking blended with floor polish to smell like sweaty feet as we walked along the corridor to Erasmus's study, where Nora paused to knock before going in. Erasmus, seated comfortably in an armchair, jumped up, disposed of the detective novel he had been reading, and stood stock still while his mother flapped her arms at him as a kind of token embrace. Having greeted Joan, he said, 'Oh . . . hello,' to me. Yes, he was surprised and there was definite pleasure in his voice, but, oh dear, how quickly his eyes slipped out of my gaze because Nora had started unpacking her basket. I leaned against the wall and watched his enthusiasm as the tins were put on the table. Grapefruit, sardines, corned beef – what hope had I against such competition?

Lunch in a restaurant with time spent in front of the cloakroom mirror trying to improve my appearance before facing the menu.

'Something simple, please, really simple, No, not steak and chips, or roast beef.' Barlows, who eat doughnuts at any time of the day, cannot understand this. They think I am being polite and encourage me to choose whatever I like. A temporary blossoming of Erasmus persuades me to make the same choice as he has made, and when the steak arrives and dribbles blood across the plate I nearly throw up. Fresh air on the downs, a brief talk with Erasmus, and a splendid diversion when his nose starts to bleed. Nora insists he lies down, and the sight of him horizontal on the grass, the wind rumpling his hair while he holds a handkerchief to his nose, persuades me I am enjoying the day after all.

A bout of high spirits carried me through tea in the Pollyanna Cafe, where other boys from the school were stuffing themselves with cakes. Chocolate eclairs, scones, jam and cream. 'I am still full up from lunch,' I explained, shivering inside my coat, not shivers from excitement but unromantic gooseflesh, because I am ill. Thank goodness for chapel, that limited the amount they could eat; Joan ate so slowly, Erasmus gobbled too quickly and I was feeling terribly sick. Outside in the dimly lit street Erasmus put on his cap and became a schoolboy again. We said goodbye, no touching of hands, no kiss. I didn't care.

What a relief to be home, to slump into a chair and not to have to be polite. My mother, after one sharp look at me, put her hand to my forehead – no thermometer to stick in my mouth, that was broken months ago – but she could judge whether I was feverish or not. She hustled me upstairs and the little luxuries of being ill now appeared – a one bar electric fire on a very short flex glowed a feeble heat from the other side of the room, and stone hot water bottles put into my bed burnt my legs before becoming icy cold. Heads popped round the door to check I was all right. I dozed off. Stealthy footsteps across the floor woke me up. What would I like to eat? Nothing. Not even a cup of Bovril? No. All I want is NOT to be sick. Cream cakes haunt my dreams, and unable to control my reflexes any longer I lean over the side of the bed and vomit into the chamber pot.

The doctor called twice a day and asked for a temperature chart to be kept. Worried eyes peered down at me out of worried faces. I was ill but well enough to manipulate the situation to my best advantage.

'Need I go back to school?' I asked in a frail voice.

'Of course not, darling, you're far too ill.'

'Please . . . need I go back to school EVER?'

'Get better, darling, get better, that's all that matters now.' I did not get better immediately but I obliged them by turning yellow, which enabled the doctor to diagnose jaundice with the possible complication of gall stones thrown in for good measure.

I had been warned that my recovery would be slow. I settled happily into invalidism until a cold snap at the beginning of March froze the reservoir and made me realise what I was missing by being in bed.

'I'm better,' I announced, 'I want to get up and go skating.'

'You must be mad,' replied my mother, 'your temperature has only been normal for a couple of days, and besides, the doctor has forbidden any exercise for weeks.' I turned a sulky face to the wall; to deny myself skating was too big a price to pay for leaving school, too big a price to pay for avoiding the school certificate next year. I tried thinking about Erasmus but the cream cakes associated with his image produced instant queasiness and proved no antidote to this craving to be out on the frozen reservoir, even if my boots were too small and the skates rusty and blunt.

I grumbled about missing a golden opportunity which might not happen again for years. It was all right for the Barlows – they could afford to go to an ice-rink whenever they liked. They didn't have to wait for the reservoir to freeze – they went skating in Oxford.

Skating in Oxford – the words written in green for envy taunted me when I closed my eyes and tried to escape into sleep. At moments like this I realised the Barlows were rich, in spite of their simple life style and clothes that nowadays no jumble sale would accept. They had a car that really worked, that took them from place to place without breaking down, unlike our second-hand wrecks which my father filled up with petrol a gallon at a time.

The frozen reservoir turned the good little patient into a querulous convalescent. When drip, drip, drip, from the trees outside my window announced the thaw had begun, I was glad, not wanting anyone else to skate if I couldn't enjoy it too.

As soon as I was declared physically fit a sense of *ennui* set in. At fifteen I had left school and there was nothing to do. Everyone seemed to be busily occupied except me, until Nora, in her fairy godmother role, suggested I should share Miss Edwardes, a music teacher who lived at Boswells, with Joan. I was delighted that my parents approved of the idea. Now life had a purpose, each day a definite shape. My mother said,

'The walk to Boswells will do you good. It will give you a chance to build up your strength.'

I had always loved music from the age of five when I heard my father playing Beethoven's first piano sonata; I was in the garden, holding two biscuits in my hand which, as soon as the full impact of the music struck me, I buried in the flower-bed – a sacrifice to the gods, perhaps, for having given me so much pleasure, a pleasure which was to become a life-long passion.

Miss Edwardes was a gawky young woman whose plain face lit up and attained a certain beauty whenever she played the piano or talked about music. She was talented, enthusiastic and patient, the ideal qualities for a teacher; under her influence I willingly practised the piano for two hours every morning in preparation for the lessons on Tuesday and Friday afternoons. I looked forward to those lessons and always set off early to make sure I reached Boswells in good time.

Often when I arrived at Boswells Miss Edwardes would be playing the piano in the drawing-room; as I waited in the hall for a convenient moment to interrupt I heard sounds coming from the other side of the door that were new and strange to an ear accustomed to Beethoven and Chopin. Miss Edwardes, contrary to her old-fashioned appearance – neat bun, long skirts and flat heeled shoes – had musical tastes that seemed to me surprisingly modern. She worshipped Scriabin, with an intensity that brought this slightly wooden composer to life. She introduced me to Debussy and revealed the mystery of his whole tone scale which produced such a weird, ghostly effect. With her encouragement I mastered his second Arabesque, which would have been quite beyond my powers a few months before. The lesson always ended when the gong boomed for tea.

Soon I was included in other activities Nora had provided for Joan. A dancing class meant the schoolroom had to be cleared; Joan and I pushed back the furniture against the wall to make space for the other children Mrs Henson brought with her. Mrs Henson ended every session with a court curtsey which she demonstrated first, holding her skirt so high that her beige knee-length knickers could be seen. Joan and I found this moment unbearably funny, which often made our curtsies very inelegant, wobbly affairs. Not that that mattered, as there was little chance of either of us becoming debutantes.

Then there were the mornings when Joan and I, alone together in the schoolroom, studied theory and harmony, which included sonata form and filling in a figured bass; compared with the lessons at school this seemed more like party games than work. While we were happily occupied with our manuscript books Miss Edwardes played the piano in the next room paying us occasional visits to see that we were getting on all right.

Nora never acted the grande dame in a village which offered ample scope for such a role had she been so inclined. However, once a week, during the term, she came near to being forced into that part, when a clutch of elderly ladies, the more cultured of the Wendover lame ducks, were rounded up by Bean, the chauffeur, to provide a captive audience for Miss Edwardes' musical talks. These ladies wore dented straw hats, navel length strings of beads, and faded dresses which, like themselves, had seen better days. While Miss Edwardes darted between piano and gramophone, telling them to listen for the entry of the violins and a theme repeated by the wind, they sat passively, registering only nostalgia for that by-gone time which the comfortable Boswells drawing-room induced. No-one ever asked any questions but dreamy expressions quickly became alert when the gong boomed and they filed across the hall into the dining-room where Joan and I handed round the scones and cake while Nora kept a tight rein on the village gossip. Tea over, Bean drove them back into Wendover, and if there was room I had a lift too. I enjoyed that moment outside my house when I emerged from the Sunbeam with a chauffeur in uniform opening the car door for me.

This was an unreal world and I loved it until Miss Edwardes decided to substitute a concert for the last musical talk of the term. Those docile ladies changed into dragon critics and the drawing-room became the Albert Hall when Joan and I played an arrangement of a Schumann symphony on two pianos. We managed it all right, and when we stood up to bow I saw that Erasmus had become part of the audience. He had crept into the room, unnoticed by me, and was sitting on the window seat clapping his hands more noisily than anyone else.

That autumn Erasmus went up to Cambridge. He came to say goodbye looking pale, unable to believe the next stage in his education would be any improvement on the previous five years! He had hated being at Marlborough.

The small green outside our house, in full view of the village street, made a most unsatisfactory venue to say the things I wanted to say, and Erasmus kept glancing at the clock tower as though time was at a premium during our desultory conversation. He drove off to a new life with a wave from the car window and I went back into the house to analyse a Schubert sonata. Miss Edwardes would expect me to come prepared for her lesson that afternoon.

Cocooned in the unhustled peace of Boswells with the routine music, lectures and dancing lessons, I began to feel like one of the family and could have resented the appearance at tea of two strangers, Helena Cornford (Frances Cornford's elder daughter) and Jill Furse, if they had not been two of the most lovely young women I had ever seen.

Not only were they lovely but they were prepared to take notice of Joan and me. After tea, heaven knows how, Nora persuaded us to play a game called Nebuchadnezzar. Choose a famous name. Delete the vowels. Find other famous names beginning with each of the consonants and mime each of those characters in turn, helping out a bewildered audience by finally miming the whole word. None of the inconsequential back-chat of charades was required, it was very much a Darwin game in which Charles Darwin often figured, Diogenes, Rasputin, Wesley and Newton being called upon to pay homage to the great man. Unlike myself Helena and Jill seemed to know what they were doing. Helena moved with the natural grace of a ballet dancer and Jill's halo of fair hair added a touch of authenticity to the biblical character she acted. I never saw Jill again, she died in childbirth after her marriage to Lawrence Whistler, but such was the impression she made at that one meeting that I mourned her death as if she had been a close friend.

Erasmus came down from Cambridge having crashed his Aunt Ruth's car on the treacherous road between Royston and Baldock. Unharmed and unrepentent, he seemed enlivened by the shock of skidding into the ditch with the car upside down on top of him. He kissed me under the mistletoe, promised vaguely to take me to the May Week Ball, and made the first of many proposals. He had enjoyed his first term at Cambridge, done all the right things from toasting muffins in front of the fire to joining the Communist party. Although he never mentioned any girls, my imagination left me in no doubt that those undergraduates, brilliant and beautiful, riding bicycles with baskets of books, were there for the sole purpose of him taking his pick. And then to make matters worse, news came of the Durst's dance. The Barlows were invited but we weren't which was perfectly understandable as the Dursts, being dyed in the wool Conservatives, had never set foot in our house. Furthermore, their lawn and prize rose bed had been ruined more than once by flooding when my brothers, for want of something better to do, had damned the stream that ran through both our gardens.

I very much wanted to go to the dance and was upset by not

receiving an invitation. My mother, instead of lecturing me on my lack of sense of proportion, decided to take up the social challenge in a spirit of *detente*. She powdered her face, put on a hat, unearthed visiting cards, and with me in tow went to pay a formal call on her neighbours. An overdue call, the Dursts having moved into the Grange four years ago. She rang the front door bell, a parlour maid appeared, cards on a silver salver, yes, Madam was at home.

Mrs Durst, graciously forgiving and with well-concealed surprise, gave us tea in the drawing-room where in two weeks' time I danced every dance with Erasmus. I still treasure that dance card, attached by a silken thread to diminutive pencil with which he wrote his name against each number – waltz, fox-trot, two-step and it should have been the Paul Jones too, because we always managed to be opposite each other when the music stopped.

At Christmas Erasmus gave me two presents – a box of handkerchiefs with the initial 'B' and a note saying: 'To keep about your person, PLEASE.' And a pair of scissors to cut my nails, with a reference to how they were always much too long.

Another, less welcome present, came from a very religious undergraduate of Oxford. He sent me a crude plaster Madonna which I, fearing ridicule from my family, hid away in my underwear. When my mother discovered it she dreaded that I might be harbouring some secret religious mania. I was easily able to reassure her.

This same young man proposed marriage to me in Swan and Edgars on the fourth floor, where we were having tea. It was neither the right place, the right time, nor the right man, and at my unequivocable response he replied 'That's clear, at any rate,' and turned his attention to a bishop's daughter, whom he married and lived happily ever after (I hope.)

When I found Freud in the county library at Aylesbury it was what I now call a Good Old God moment; with so many books on the shelves I needed divine guidance to pick out the one which opened up a whole chunk of life to me. I began with 'Psychopathology of Everyday Life', and graduated to the 'Interpretations of Dreams.' At last a valid excuse to think more deeply about myself and if necessary blame others for my faults and failings.

My trips to Aylesbury increased as I took out more and more books from the library. Unable to believe there wasn't somewhere a young man in all this enthusiasm my mother questioned me closely, but was finally convinced by the hours I spent reading and taking notes that this was a genuine interest, *pro tem*, she hadn't much faith in a capricious sixteen year old.

'I want to be a psychologist,' I announced, and amidst the murmurs of concern and approval was the overriding relief that the problem daughter had at last found something she really wanted to do. Money, ever scarce, would be squeezed from the trust to send me to the Regent Street Polytechnic where I would be crammed to matriculate at the end of the academic year, but where could I stay in London? I told Nora the problem while we were having tea at Boswells, and with a wave of her magic wand, hey presto, she fixed me up to stay in Ladbroke Grove with Cosmo and Frances Gordon.

3

I arrived at 43 Ladbroke Grove on a blustery October night, having caught a train to a station of that name, not realising this involved a walk up a hill with a heavy suitcase to carry, and a hat which every gust of wind nearly blew off my head. The dark street with poor lighting and a pavement slippery from fallen leaves were added hazards. By the time I reached No 43 I was out of breath and thoroughly dishevelled. I rang the bell and watched through the stained glass panel a tall, pale lady with white hair wearing a long velvet dress walk down the passage towards me. This was Mrs Gordon, Frances she soon became.

My bedroom was on the third floor, at the back of the house which, unlike sprawling country houses, went up and up. It overlooked the gardens of Lansdowne Road, 'Where Erasmus was born,' Mrs Gordon said, unwittingly striking the right note.

I unpacked my case, carefully stowing away my clothes, determined to be tidy. It was a new experience to have a room of my own and feel my belongings belonged to me. At home I had moved from sleeping higgledy-piggledy in the nursery with my brothers to sharing a bedroom with my sister. We borrowed each other's things without asking permission; to keep something for oneself was considered greedy, materialistic and selfish.

Out on the landing I looked over the banisters down the well of the stairs and saw all the closed doors I had to pass before braving the sitting-room where Cosmo Gordon sat in front of the fire reading a book. Cosmo was always reading a book, except when he was eating the meals, most lovingly prepared by his wife. I had never met anyone so domesticated as Frances before. She counted every penny and if fish was twopence cheaper at the other end of Notting Hill Gate then that is where she would go to buy it – on foot of course.

Frances was a domestic saint who sacrificed herself to make

an unmanageable house a joy for anyone living in it. There
was always a fire in the sitting-room, and the table at the other
end of the room was laid with shining silver cutlery, giving the
illusion of gracious living even if the dinner had been prepared by herself under primitive conditions in a dark basement kitchen and sent up to the next floor by means of a
creaking hand-drawn lift. There was very little domestic help
apart from a faithful retainer, who looked after Cosmo's
invalid mother on the first floor. A Mrs Wolfe came in during
the evenings and enabled Frances to change into the long
velvet dress in which I first saw her. It felt like promotion when
I was allowed to carry the plates from the table to the lift and
shout down the shaft to Mrs Wolfe to send up the next
course.

Cosmo was sweet and gentle, qualities which must have
made it difficult for him to survive as a soldier in the Great
War. I discovered about his war record by chance. I was wrapping up a parcel in the sitting-room when suddenly he put
down his book and rather shamefacedly asked me to stop.

'I can't bear the sound of crackling paper,' he said, 'it
reminds me of being in the trenches and the shells falling
nearer and nearer,' and then he began blinking as if to shut
out the memory.

'I always thought the next bomb was going to fall on
me.'

He was a dear man who inspired great affection among the
Darwin clan. They preferred his nose-in-book and head-in-
the-clouds intellectuality to the down to earth unbridled
domesticity of his wife, although it was through her loving
care he had been nursed back to health after years of trench
warfare, in which he won the Military Cross.

'Cosmo is *wonderful*,' would be set off by 'Frances is always
talking about gas stoves and the prices of things.' However, on
one occasion at least, the two worlds overlapped. Driving
along a lonely road in Scotland, Cosmo suddenly told his
friend, Geoffrey Keynes, who was at the wheel, to stop. They
had just passed a large swede which must have fallen off a cart,
and Cosmo, being a true Scot, could not bear to see it go to
waste. Ignoring Geoffrey Keynes's disapproving face he got
out of the car, ran back and picked up the free gift, perhaps
anticipating his wife's pleasure when he presented it to her

that night. Such behaviour was incomprehensible to Geoffrey Keynes who, if the story is true, refused to speak to Cosmo again until his anger had died down –a full ten minutes at least

My mother, guessing I would lose no time in building up a stock of admirers in London, took the precaution of writing to Frances. She asked her to check on what I was doing, where I was going, and with whom I was spending my time if ever I went out in the evening. Frances in a terse note refused to do any such thing but she soon learned to distinguish between the voices of the two young men who dominated my life during those happy months, and would call me to the phone saying, 'It's the polite one again,' or 'the nervous one has rung back.'

The polite one was Robin Pearce, a friend of Denis Ewer, whom I met that summer. He had long wavy hair and looked like Pan, and should have been permanently sitting among the beech trees in Bucks, playing his pipe, instead of painting rather dull pictures of trees, which no-one wanted to buy. He was a romantic figure who fulfilled my girlish dreams of an artist living a bohemian life in a Chelsea garret. Actually the garret was in Earls Court, and Robin supplemented what he did not earn from his paintings by working as manager at the Everyman Cinema in Hampstead. When I met him in Great Missenden he had a summer tan, but seeing him again in the autumn I was struck by his unhealthy appearance. His hair matched his face, and his face matched the shantung shirts he always wore. He smelled of TCP. I told my mother about this, and she jumped to the conclusion that the mouth infection he was trying to cure was caused by gonorrhea. *Amor vincit omnia*. In spite of my mother's warning, his seedy looks and the smell of TCP I went willingly to his flat, which resembled a set for *La Boheme*; stove, dormer window, threadbare carpet and of course a bed. We listened to Beethoven's eighth symphony in front of the fire, following the score, with a kiss at the end of the first movement and a suggestion that we might move over to the bed when the music had finished. I took fright and grabbing my coat and bag made a dash down the stairs to safety. Robin was prepared to bide his time, and when not trying to seduce me he educated me instead. We went round the galleries, pausing in front of the pictures he liked. Van Gogh's yellow chair was one of his favourites. We stood in front of it for ages and he made me notice things I would never have seen if he had not been there to point them out. Afterwards there might be supper in an Italian restaurant where another artist, William Scott, who shared the flat with Robin, often joined us. William Scott was never in the flat when I visited Robin and it took a chance meeting at a private view, a quarter of a century later, for me to find out why.

'You're the girl Robin was always trying to seduce,' he recalled. 'I was never allowed in the flat when you came. Hours and hours I spent trudging up an down Earls Court Road in the rain. I like to think. . . .' He paused, and I quickly apologised for all that bad weather exercise which had been in vain.

If Robin had kept quiet while we lay on the bed my ardour might never have cooled, but he would talk, and it was what he said that eventually put me off. Post Marie Stopes and pre Masters and Johnson, the theories he expounded were entirely his own, the result of lengthy research, no doubt!

.'Never,' he said, 'make love in the nude. It is far more exciting with one's clothes on.' If he had seen what I was wearing underneath my dress he might have modified this golden rule. The thick, shapeless woollen vest I wore was an improvement on the 'liberty bodice' I had only recently discarded. It was an extremely ugly object which should have carried a warning label saying 'not suitable for love making.' My knickers with elasticated legs almost reaching to the knee were veritable sex killers unless someone had kinky tastes, which perhaps Robin had for all I know; we never went so far as for me to find out.

I admired Robin for his good manners – he was punctual and whatever the weather insisted on seeing me home to Ladbroke Grove after an evening out. But as our relationship failed to progress, his manners slackened, and by the time I was immersed in taking my matric he had become extremely casual. We arranged to meet for lunch in his flat. I rang the bell and William Scott let me in. Minutes ticked away as I waited, becoming more and more agitated. Eventually Robin arrived, decanted some dubious slices of ham from a paper bag on to my dusty plate and added a few lettuce leaves one of which concealed an outsize slug. All that combined with the invigilator's face when I entered the examination room half an hour late was enough to shatter my dreams of an artist's life in a garret.

The final break came one afternoon, soon after that, when lying on the bed Robin decided to give a lecture on free love, which led via the possibility of pregnancy to the subject of abortion.

'The last girl I lived with got pregnant,' he said quite chattily, as though that was just a trivial event, 'and I fixed up an abortion for her quite easily. A bit expensive of course, but her family coughed up, they had to, they couldn't afford a scandal.'

He gave a little laugh and explained how they were a distinguished legal family, one I had vaguely heard of. Shocked to the core I involuntarily moved away until I was almost falling off the edge of the bed. I lay quite still, gazing up at the sky through the dormer window. A clean, blue, rain washed sky which somehow reminded me of Erasmus. *He* would never talk glibly about an abortion. *He* had principles. I never told Robin what I felt. I just said goodbye and ran down the stairs out of his life, wishing there was some means – a scrubbing brush and a bottle of disinfectant – to erase him from my memory.

The other man in my life, the 'nervous one' as Frances called him, was Reg Butler. He wore a bow tie, smoked a pipe, had a bold appreciative stare and was conveniently placed studying architecture on the floor above the one where I worked. Discovering him in the bleak Polytechnic was like striking gold in barren waste. We eyed each other across the refectory, gave half smiles as we passed on the stairs and might have gone on like that for weeks if I hadn't taken the initiative and dropped a load of books at his feet.

'What is the psychological reason for that?' He asked. My heart sank. In those few words I detected an accent. My mother would disapprove, and of course she did. After his visit she said she could smell the cabbage cooking as soon as he entered the room – in other words he was common. Twenty years later, flicking over the pages of a glossy magazine in a dentist's waiting room, I saw Reg's face looking up at me – the same bow tie and pipe, a little less hair – this 'common little man' had achieved international fame as a sculptor. There was a lengthy article about his controversial work 'The Political Prisoner.'

Reg also took it upon himself to educate me, only unlike Robin's, his lectures were never horizontal. In the ABC around the corner from the Polytechnic he held forth on the purpose of life and whether architecture was the mother of art – or perhaps it was the other way round, I can't be sure. He also coached me in physics; leaning across the green glass table he tried to explain the inexplicable while our cups of tea grew cold and the waitress impatient. On the morning of the physics examination a postcard from him arrived and beneath the good wishes Reg had written the Boyle's Law formula: $P = \dfrac{1}{V}$

Reg had a childhood friend called Jo, whom I had never met but soon felt I knew quite well owing to his tiresome habit of bringing her into the conversation whenever our relationship seemed to be most happy and secure. They both lived in Brookman's Park and there, in that plebian setting, she did incongruous things like dance barefoot among the snowdrops in her nightie, with the wind blowing through her long hair, which enchanted him and I found nauseating.

Desperate to keep up, I retaliated with stories about *my* childhood friend, stories which became more and more exaggerated until there was nothing left but to pretend Erasmus and I had become engaged. Reg was gratifyingly upset, but no sooner had I chalked up this point in my favour when an unforeseen event wiped the slate clean. Quite by chance, during the rush hour, fate decreed that Reg and my sister should meet on a crowded underground platform. Naturally he mentioned what was foremost in his mind – my 'engagement' to Erasmus – and she, taken by surprise, was unable to control her amazement, and exclaimed 'Nonsense', flatly denying the truth of my short-lived triumph. Reg made an ugly scene from which I emerged much wiser with one lesson learned, not, I regret, *never* to tell lies, but be prepared for the unexpected if you *do*.

When I married Erasmus and Reg married Jo, Reg's dry comment sounded like an epitaph, 'We have both done what was expected of us,' he said.

With so much emotional turmoil going on my studies inevitably suffered, and my mother foretold disaster.

'If you don't stop gadding about with young men,' she said, 'you'll fail your exam and all the money we've spent on you will be wasted.' This familiar theme produced short term results. For a while I would spend contrite evenings in Ladbroke Grove, poring over my books, until the telephone rang and Frances called, 'Biddy, it's for you.'

When Hugh came down from Cambridge he went out as much as I did; and in order to know which of us must switch off the lights and lock the front door a note was left on the hall table with our names on it. If Hugh got home first he would not only cross out his name but also embellish the paper with rude comments, 'What in the hell are you doing?' or 'Why so damned late?' I never dared do the same for him.

The following term Hugh invited me to a party in Cambridge. Unlike today's flexiplans, everything had to be fixed weeks ahead, and the sleeping arrangements gone into in detail. Letters were exchanged between my mother and an unknown hostess to make sure I would be 'all right', that being the euphemism used for ensuring I was alone in bed at night.

I spent the evening sitting in the same armchair as Erasmus, not exactly in an embrace but the nearest thing to it so far. Someone drank too much and was sick all over the floor. For the first and only time I tasted gin. A glass full of gin, either by mistake or as a joke, was handed to me when I asked for lemonade. One gulp and the aversion therapy was complete. When John Cornford arrived late at the party all conversation momentarily stopped. Why, I don't know, unless our silence was prophetic; he died not long after that, fighting for the Communists in Spain.

When Tam developed scarlet fever, my mother readily agreed to Nora's suggestion that I should spend the weekends at Boswells rather than risk infection by going home. I resented this arrangement, presented to me as a *fait accompli*, until Erasmus met me at the station, his term having ended before mine. I lost no time in asking him to help me with my maths homework and together, after dinner, we sat in the schoolroom solving all the problems bar one, which took so long that I gave up and went upstairs to bed, leaving him to struggle with it on his own. I was in the bath when he shouted 'Eureka' from the other side of the door. He had found the answer and each stage had to be explained to me while I stood wrapped in a towel, shivering and dripping wet.

It was spring. Daffodils, battered by wind, made a bright splodge of yellow in the garden and crocuses sprang up under the weeping elm. When we walked to the Rising Sun on Hamden Common it was warm enough to take our drinks outside, and on our way home Joan and I hunted for primroses. There was a lot of sitting around, listening to the gramophone and on a Saturday evenings the ritual of a dinner party which consisted mostly of family, a few guests from London and never anyone local. Alan always changed into his velvet smoking jacket and replaced his cotton tie with a smart black bow. Nora changed too, but out of what and into what I don't remember. Her disregard for clothes was part of the 'that will do' philosophy which she recognised as a reaction against her mother's perfectionism.

'We could never dress as other children dressed,' she complained, 'We always had to be different. I remember once my mother made me and Ruth wear party dresses with fur round the neck.'

Years later I behaved in exactly the same way as Ida Darwin. I designed dresses for my daughters more suitable for the *corp de ballet* in Swan Lake than a birthday party with their little friends. When Nora saw them in their finery her only comment was,

'I suppose this is something you've got to be allowed to get out of your system.'

On those Saturday evenings the gong boomed extra loudly, and when we filed into the dining-room my lack of a long-sleeved silk dress became acute. The parlour-maids, in starched aprons and frilly caps, standing with their backs to the sideboard, cast deprecating looks down their noses, I felt sure, at my tweed frock.

During one of those weekends I overheard a conversation between a guest and Nora. I was in the bedroom and they were outside in the corridor talking about me. The guest said,

'What a charming girl, do tell me about her, please.'

Nora replied: 'She comes from a mad Irish family in the village.'

'She's charming, absolutely charming,' repeated the guest, and after a pause a seemingly reluctant Nora agreed: 'Yes, yes . . . she is charming, I suppose.' I had never thought of myself as charming and I was delighted that the guest thought so, but why Nora's hesitant enthusiasm?

I hadn't yet learned that Darwins are suspicious of charm. Charm for them is a synomym for superficial and insincere. Nora was in fact paying me a compliment by not readily endorsing her friend's comment.

After a lot of last minute cramming I sat my matriculation in a heat wave and passed. My father was delighted, my mother astonished and my pleasure muted by the feeling that somehow I had let down the side. No one in our family could pass exams; they were too artistic, too creative, too eager for self expression, attributes my parents valued more than my certificate with six boring subjects written on it.

Erasmus came down to congratulate me. He seemed genuinely pleased with my exam result. I picked him a rose from a bush in the garden and he stuck it in his button hole and actually blew me a kiss as he drove off for the long vac term. We saw each other again quite soon. My cousin Ambrose invited my sister and me to stay in Cambridge. Sleeping accommodation was vetted, letters exchanged and eventually we were having tea in Erasmus' room. Erasmus provided the food; crumpets and cucumber sandwiches; Ambrose provided the conversation with intelligent comments from Gill, while I sat self-consciously silent on the sofa in my new dress of rose pink voile, unable to move because the huge puffed sleeves were as inhibiting as a straitjacket.

Ambrose approved of Erasmus; everything seemed to be going well until Erasmus mentioned his forthcoming trip to Russia – and then the atmosphere froze. Ambrose disapproved of anyone left of centre. He was only prepared to mix with us because we were cousins. And vice versa.

Erasmus was by now a fully paid up member of the Communist Party which I, having had enough of my parents' politics, found rather silly. He went to Russia full of enthusiasm for the Soviet way of life and wrote back long screeds. Visits to hospitals, schools and a crèche did not make enthralling reading, particularly now that I was being wooed by a young man who had been introduced to me by a matchmaking friend of my parents. We were ideally suited, she said, and to begin with that seemed to be true. He did delightful things like serenade me on his guitar and send bunches of roses in cellophane. But he had crinkly fair hair which I did not like, blue eyes which he kept open for maximum effect, and he was inordinately vain. Vanity was a fault I could easily recognise in others as I was guilty of it myself. If there was a mirror handy I always glanced in it, and he did too. Sometimes our eyes met, not in a loving look but with one of embarrassment. What counted against him most was a cultural inadequacy. I was shocked to find in an art gallery that he couldn't tell a Cezanne from a Van Gogh.

It was a paradox of the thirties that parents with liberal left wing views almost invariably sent their children to Nazi Germany when they wanted their minds broadened by a spell abroad. My sister had studied art in Stuttgart, my brother attended Tübingen University and Erasmus stayed near the Black Forest with a schoolmaster's family after he left school.

We all hated Hitler, despised his philosophy of the master race and dreaded him beginning another world war but the exchange rate was good and as there was enough money left in the education trust it was decided Germany was the place where I should go. With one proviso, of course; the right family must be found. My mother scanned the columns in *The Lady*, my father scratched his head and wrote to a few left-wing friends. They were both visibly relieved when nothing suitable turned up. Fearing my chances of going abroad might peter out I consulted the oracle, and as usual Nora provided the answer. Miraculously a Professor Muller from Cologne was coming to stay at Boswells, and the following week she brought him to have tea; a bespectacled, sad little man with a long tale of woe guaranteed to appeal to my parents. He was a Roman Catholic with a wife and ever increasing family to support but unable to get a job because Hitler hated the Rhineland Catholics almost as much as he hated the Jews.

By the time we got up from the tea table everything was fixed. I was to stay with the Muller family and study Chemistry and Zoology at the University, where Dr Muller had friends. This plan had Nora's blessing and although my mother fretted about the white slave traffic it was agreed I should be allowed to travel on my own.

I kissed my parents goodbye with only a momentary qualm because Erasmus was waiting to drive me to the station. He ensured that I and my trunk were safely on the train. Reg Butler saw me off at Liverpool Street and the crinkly-haired suitor turned up unexpectedly at Harwich to help me on the boat, where a handsome Dutchman bought me lunch and saw that I had made the right connection for Cologne when we docked at the Hook. Travelling on my own!

4

The Muller family was planning to go to the States before the situation worsened in Nazi Germany. With three little girls and another baby on the way they were patently hard up; meals consisted mostly of potatoes, and when I came to pay for my keep Dr Muller asked me to keep the money and sent it to him when they were settled in St Louis. A request with which I naturally kept faith.

My time at Cologne University had a Kafka craziness which left a confused memory of young men with swastika stained souls beneath the innocent white coats they wore for work at the laboratory bench. Women, busy fulfilling Hitler's ideal of *Kinder, Kuche und Kirche* did not study chemistry and I was very much an oddity among all the male students, who never let an opportunity pass to ridicule me.

What I had read in the newspaper at home I now saw with my own eyes: *Judische Geschaft* scrawled across boarded-up shop windows; Professor Muller's fear when a Jewish friend spoke to him in the street; and the guests at the Mullers' house who were struck dumb with petrified horror by a child playing with a monkey puppet and making it give the Nazi salute.

The make-believe world of opera provided an escape from the abrasive life at the university and the sad Mullers' home. Dr Muller organised me into going to *Parsifal* with black bread sandwiches and the score. My student's ticket enabled me to sit on a wooden bench high up in the gods. Never having been to the opera before I had no idea what was in store. By the end of the overture I was hooked, completely hooked, and when the final curtain came down I wanted it to begin all over again. From now on I did without lunch, walked to the university instead of taking the tram; no sacrifice was too great to save money to obtain my fix. Dr Muller, who had introduced me to my dope now complained,

'When people ask what you saw in Germany, all you'll be able to say is the inside of the opera house''.' Astonishing what

48

stupid things intelligent people say! My trip abroad had achieved its goal, my mind had been broadened and a life-long love affair with opera began.

Erasmus wrote with a plan which appealed to me greatly, although I knew it was destined never to come off. Imagining the decision was mine to make he suggested I should go canoeing down the Rhine with him and his friend John Kidd. What a wonderful picture this invitation conjured up: sunshine, fresh air, exercise, sparkling water, paddles going swish-swish and at night, in the moonlight, on the river bank, two tents without even the tent pegs touching, one for him and John, the other for me. My mother saw it differently. 'There would be endless temptations,' she wrote, and the answer was 'no', underlined several times.

The term ended not with a bang but a whimper. I took leave of my fellow students, happy never to see them again, but when it came to saying goodbye to the professor a controlled whimper brought a lump to my throat. He had a Jewish grandmother, I knew, and at any moment he might lose his job to suffer the lot of those who weren't of pure Aryan stock. He shook me by the hand, wished me good luck. His sad face fleetingly lightened as he said,

'*Sie mussen sauber arbeiten, Fraulein Black*,' remembering, perhaps, the explosive mixture in a test tube that made me fall into his arms.

When I returned to England I was met by the entire family at Great Missenden station. In my absence, my parents had moved to Little Kingshill, exchanging a beautiful house for an ugly one, both of them equally inconvenient to run. We were no longer in walking distance of Boswells and if Erasmus wanted to see me he had to come by car. Erasmus loved driving and it may be it was that love, rather than the love of me, that increased his visits.

The crinkly-haired Adonis appeared with a new intellectual look, as though he had undergone a crash course in culture during my time away. Instead of the tango *Oh, Fraulein Greta*, he played Ravel's *Bolero* on the gramophone, which brought him no nearer to my musical taste. He wrote poems about unrequited love, and wisely avoiding the French Impressionists he concentrated on modern art, using his brother's sculptures as a bait to draw me to Oxford, where his parents had a house off the Banbury Road.

My mother, detecting a revving up of the emotional tempo, laid down rules for behaviour: cuddling on the drawing-room sofa was permissible and kissing, too, was allowed, provided feet remained firmly on the ground and lips never met lips. How easy to feel that guilty frisson of having gone too far. Perhaps *that* was what she intended, who knows?

Erasmus returned to Cambridge for his last year at the same time that I became a student at University College in London. As usual he came to say goodbye. There was a kiss, vague talk about marrying me one day, and a promise to take me to the May Week Ball, none of which I took seriously until a letter arrived from him soon after he had gone. He invited me to stay for the weekend at his grandmother's house in Cambridge. My mother dipped her head like a wise old bird and said,

'He means business,' I thought, Oh please God, not another proposal. Erasmus had been proposing marriage to me since I was fifteen.

My mother raised no objection to my spending a weekend with Lady Darwin at The Orchard.

But what about my clothes? A week-end with Lady Darwin required something special. A new white collar would perhaps rejuvenate my winter frock, but what was I going to change into for dinner? Where was that long-sleeved silk dress? The shiny, slippery, turquoise answer to my problem hung in my friend's cupboard. We were almost the same size and it fitted me – more or less.

I packed my suitcase with my shoes, wrapped in newspaper, at the bottom. Newspaper separated underwear from the borrowed turquoise dress, which had most of the *News Chronicle* between its folds to stop if from creasing.

Erasmus was at Cambridge station to greet me with an awkward kiss under the brim of my hat, and a huge Daimler – his grandmother's car. I had been to The Orchard once before with Nora and Joan but now I was here as Erasmus's girl friend which in the Victorian eyes of Lady Darwin clearly implied something more exclusive than a casual relationship. Her warm welcome coupled with the enthusiastic response from her friends to whom she introduced me, made me wonder whether this wasn't another case of mistaken identity, the fancy dress party all over again.

A maid relieved me of my suitcase, carrying it up to the bedroom, which overlooked the large garden shrouded in mist. The familiar smell of furniture polish and pot-pourri reminded me of Boswells, only here there was no hint of Nora's spartan 'that will do'. The accent was on comfort – snowy towels galore, extra rugs across the foot of the four poster, and on the bedside table, the height of luxury – a tin of digestive biscuits in case hunger struck during the night. Before I had time to unpack, the gong sounded downstairs where Erasmus, very much in charge, ushered me into the dining-room, standing close to me, assuming he would be put next to where I sat.

When lunch was over Lady Darwin suggested I should have a rest. She said I looked tired after my journey and it would do me good to have a little sleep. Feeling like an invalid in a very expensive nursing home I went up to my bedroom to find that the maid had unpacked. The pieces of newspaper lay neatly folded in the empty suitcase, my tatty underwear, which I had never expected anyone to see, was stowed away in drawers, and the shiny, slippery, turquoise dress hung alone in the heavy mahogany wardrobe. I lay down on the bed and immediately the maid appeared with a hot water bottle in a knitted cover. She took the rug off the sofa and wrapped it round my feet, showed me the bell and asked me to ring if there was anything I wanted.

A tap on the door woke me up and the maid told me that 'Mr Erasmus' was waiting in the hall to take me out. We walked through the dank, autumnal streets to his lodgings in Jesus Lane, where in this highly privileged setting he delivered a speech on behalf of the Communist Party while buttering the bread we had toasted in front of the fire. He poured out tea, cut big wedges of Fuller's frosted walnut cake, and then when conversation dwindled to question and answer he asked me to marry him. I said 'no', but the 'no' had a hint of 'maybe', because Erasmus behind the tea cups appealed to me, and if politics had not cast a shadow over the domestic scene I might have been tempted to say 'yes'.

A fortnight later I was off to Oxford to stay with crinkly-hair and his family who fascinated me because they did shocking things like exchange wives, go into monasteries, and have illegitimate children. My mother heartily disapproved of such behaviour, particularly of the brother. It was rumoured he had done something unmentionable with a dog, an Alsatian, I think it was; what he'd done I never knew, but it was enough to make her very doubtful about letting me go. Crinkly-hair had charm, and thanks to his powers of persuasion I found myself again being welcomed into the family as The Girl Friend. The similarity ended there. Chilly house, prickly relationships, and a gong which summoned us not to the table, but to morning prayers.

We assembled in the sitting-room, the char-woman, crinkly-hair, his mother, and an architect son, who, hit by one of the many scandals, now lived at home with his three year old daughter. We knelt on cushions, while the *pater familias* stood behind a chair. He cast fierce looks beneath his white bushy eyebrows but whenever I caught his eye, the look changed to an unmistakable leer.

Anna, the three year old, and I soon became close friends, and when crinkly-hair returned to London, leaving me behind feeling unwell, her father joined in our games, which included a doll's funeral with a flower-lined soap-box coffin and a grave in the garden. The company of a mature man was excitingly new. We soon became a trio; Anna, her father and me. At first my hostess approved of the laughter and fun, maintaining that was just what her son and grand-daughter needed, but after a few days she became alarmed by the ever increasing animation and wrote to my mother about her fear of yet another complicated entanglement within the family. Mercifully, perhaps, before the storm broke I was rushed into a nursing home for an emergency operation on my appendix.

My mother always said I would flirt with the undertaker who measured me for my coffin. Although the surgeon wasn't the undertaker, I *was* feeling half dead when he came to examine me. I still rallied my feminine wiles to beg him not to blemish my smooth, white stomach with an ugly scar. The result was a small, neat incision of which he was immensely proud and I thought was as much due to my charms as his skill.

The pains before and after the operation were nothing compared to the horror of the anaesthetic. In those days, which seem like the dark ages now, there were no pre-medicals, no drifting off into sleep while counting up to ten; I was wheeled into the operating theatre wide awake and a masked figure had to hold me down until the chloroform rape was complete.

As soon as Erasmus heard of my operation he borrowed a car and drove out to visit me. Crinkly-hair did exactly the same thing and their visits followed one after the other. Erasmus sat at the end of the bed, caressing my feet while reading the newspaper he had brought for my benefit. Crinkly-hair, loaded with flowers and sweets seemed to have only one idea in his head which I quickly disillusioned with a cry of pain when he tried to come near me.

I returned home after a week to be cos>setted and although I enjoyed the attention during the day, nights were a drawn out misery through lack of sleep. Memory of the anaesthetic kept me awake. I lay in bed, staring into the dark, not daring to close my eyes for fear of losing control of my thoughts, which could never escape from the fight that I had had with the masked figure in the hospital. My mother explained to Nora that I was highly strung and nervy and Nora suggested a few days on the bracing East coast as a remedy. The family always enjoyed going to Hillside in winter, and if my sister and I joined in the party, they'd be delighted. Grateful for anything that might speed up my convalescence, my mother agreed, assuming Nora would be there in charge. When we arrived we found only Erasmus, Martin Pollock and Janet, his girl friend. We reacted as though we had landed in a brothel. Martin and Janet were sharing the same bedroom. Should we go home straight away or remain and show our disapproval? Actually, we did neither. We stayed and thoroughly enjoyed ourselves. Erasmus cooked endless bacon and eggs and his navy blue fisherman's jersey smelled of frying when we kissed each other good-night.

No pressure was brought to bear on me to start work again at University College as the pains which had caused the operation continued even though my appendix was out. These pains, due to adhesions, the doctor said, grew conveniently worse at the thought of mornings spent in a stuffy lecture theatre followed by afternoons in the laboratory, one eye pressed to a microscope, watching amoebae which had nothing more exciting to do than to divide. And the chaos of my loose-leaf note book, how could I bring myself to face that again?

I lost weight, slept badly and fretted about the family finances, with which I could not help. No-one mentioned the word 'malingering' and I was encouraged to rest more, which gave me more time to think – the last thing I needed to do. Cod liver oil and malt, Menadex, vitamin pills failed to pull me out of my decline and every week my weight card, after standing on the chemist's scales, showed a few more pounds lost.

We talked a lot, my mother and I – there was plenty of time to talk. She regretted my lack of resources and that my only interest seemed to be young men. Lengthy discussions, that went round and round, with always the same topic at the hub of the conversation wheel. A good Quaker, she said, has only one proposal –the one she accepts, and here was I, the daughter of a very good Quaker, with a whole string of young men wanting to marry me. Disgusting, no wonder I felt ill. Settling for one would give me a purpose in life. The word-bashing continued until the string of young men had been short-listed to two.

I sat at the dining-room table and wrote to Erasmus while my mother stood behind my chair, urging me on to tell him that I had finally made up my mind to marry someone else.

With perfect timing, no sooner had the letter been posted than the telephone rang with an invitation from Nora to go to Elgar's Dream of Gerontius. Erasmus would be there, she said, unaware that that was no longer a bait. My mother decided my sister should go in my place, and suggested that instead of looking aggrieved I should start preparing for my bottom drawer, which meant stitching daisies on to a tray cloth while my thoughts hacked away at the past. The invitation to the Dream of Gerontius had had a most disturbing effect. All that the Barlow family had done to widen my musical horizons came back to taunt me as I sat there sewing. Nora had taken me to Bach's St Matthew Passion in the Albert Hall and we had eaten a healthy, starchy lunch during the long interval, in the open air. Thanks to her I discovered the strength of Bach's Mass in B minor. If it hadn't been for Nora I should never have studied with Miss Edwardes and been introduced to the modern composers. And Nora had stage-managed my stay in Germany – she was really responsible for my love of opera. The Dream of Gerontius became a symbol of all that I was giving up. From now on Ravel's Bolero would be the background music to my life.

My father handed me Erasmus's reply to my letter while I was still half asleep in bed. The beginning: "Darling Biddy, Your letter has sunk in now, and I'll try and say what I want to say without too much fuss," was enough to make me cry, but the ending, with a Blake quotation

Does the Eagle know what is in the pit
Or wilt thou go ask the Mole?
Can Wisdom be put in a silver rod
Or Love in a golden bowl?

produced such an outburst that tears almost obliterated the cool, dignified words with which he took his dismissal. My father, seeing me distraught, called my mother. My mother alerted my sister, who informed my brother, and they all stood round the bed, not knowing what to say or do to comfort me. My father brought me breakfast in bed, with a flower on the tray, which only made matters worse, because treating me like an invalid was no cure for my sense of loss, which hurt like toothache in the heart.

The next day I went to stay in Oxford. The house was dark and quiet, the meals long and slow, and only my future mother-in-law and father-in-law were there. I attended family prayers, helped with the washing-up, called my hostess Two-Ma (at her request) and did my best to feel like one of the family, while growing more and more frantic, until by the end of the week I knew I must escape from these lovely people who were driving me mad.

I wrote to Erasmus, explaining I must get away and asking him to come and fetch me as soon as he could. I was a princess, imprisoned in a tower, wringing my hands in despair waiting to be rescued by my prince on a white charger – or rather Erasmus in his parent's car. I waited in vain. Erasmus's reply, on a postcard, should have been sent to me in Oxford, but it went instead to my home address. My mother read with dismay that the rejected suitor was willing to fetch me at any time and drive me anywhere I chose. Shocked by my 'duplicity' she upbraided me down the phone. What did I think I was

doing asking favours from Erasmus now? *NOW. NOW. NOW.* I
must stay where I was and return by coach as planned on
Monday. On that day the man I had decided to marry was
coming down to ask permission from my father for a formal
engagment. The ring had already been bought and in my
imagination would be produced from his waistcoat pocket.

I never saw the engagement ring, because fate, chance,
God's computer or what-you-will decreed that at the precise
moment I came out of the house to go and meet Crinkly-Hair
at the station Erasmus, in the farm van, should pass by. He
stopped, and offered me a lift to Great Missenden.

Neither of us spoke a word during the short drive but by the
time I got out of the van my mind was made up – Erasmus was
the one I wanted to marry, not the man who would soon be
getting off the train with the engagement ring in his
pocket.

Parental patience had finally run out and only my brother,
Tam, retained his sense of humour. He said the last few weeks
had been like the run-up to a General Election, with my
mother voting for Crinkly-Hair while my father canvassed for
Erasmus. He talked about reading the ticker tape and teased
me that I had burnt my boats and now there was nobody
wanting to marry me. My mother, exasperated by my treatment of the young man in whom she had invested a lot of
affection, declared I was in no fit state to become engaged to
anybody, and sensing that Erasmus was in favour again, made
plans to send me to Germany.

However, Erasmus stole a march on her by becoming my
confidant. I poured out my feelings to him – feelings which
appeared more dottily irrational than they were because pride
prevented me from admitting that the letter about my intention to marry someone else had been a mistake.

Poor Erasmus, brought up in a family where any show of
emotion, apart from an occasional 'Oh dear', was *de trop,*
managed well with his first mental patient. He wrote, 'If I were
a disinterested observer, I can imagine saying to you, My girl,
your state of mind is bloody awful, and you've got to take
yourself in hand. . .'" There followed good, sound, sensible
advice about working out a line of action and sticking to it,
which was spoilt at the end of the letter by his saying that,
'unfortunately, I am NOT a disinterested observer.'

I replied with a whole page of piffle about the advantages of platonic friendship and was relieved when his next letter expressed a sceptical view on that subject. The correspondence continued, purging the past of recent unhappiness, and enabling us, when we met again at a hockey match, to slip back into our childhood larky relationship. The cold air, the bare legs, and the chilly orange slices at half time all helped, why, I don't know.

Erasmus invited me to his birthday, a 'that will do' affair with a cake bought from the village bakery and decorated with his initials by the cook. I was the only guest. After tea, we borrowed the car and drove to Amersham, where a fortune teller read the future from my palm. Having been told everything I wanted to hear, I was sufficiently encouraged to baffle Erasmus further when we came to say goodbye, as his letter shows:

'I don't know whether to tell myself that because you apparently wanted me to kiss you, and I did, that you love me and that you've changed your mind and all you said before counts for nothing, or whether to say no, of course she wouldn't change her mind after all the worrying and struggle she's obviously been through. . . .'

In the midst of all this emotional turmoil Erasmus sat the part two of his Tripos, and with that behind him he was free to do what was really uppermost in his mind – return to Wendover, see me again, and make some sense of my nonsensical behaviour. A chest of drawers had to be taken from Boswells to his aunt's house in the White Horse hills. The perfect excuse for time alone together. It was the first of June, a sultry morning, with soft blue sky and the sun just courageous enough to penetrate the haze. A wonderful scent wafted up from the bean flowers in bloom. I only have to catch a whiff of that same scent now to recapture the happiness as we sat together in the front of the van with the chest of drawers lurching around in the back. The countryside was white on white with cow parsley and may against a landscape of chalk.

When we arrived at a pink-washed house with the extraordinary name of 'The Dog, Trip The Daisy,' Helen Barlow walked briskly down the flagstone path to greet us. I had met her many times since the children's fancy dress party. She was quite a familiar figure sitting side-saddle on her horse, Joey,

cantering over the hills, always prepared to stop and exchange
a few words with anyone she recognised, including me.
Buxom and jolly -she was a different species from the Darwins. Her house had a different smell, too. Less pot-pourri,
more floor polish, and none of the missing link.

Lunch was cooked by Mrs Wagstaff and brought into the
dining room at the tinkle of a little bell. I don't remember
what we ate but it must have been good because Helen Barlow
was without a puritanical streak. She could love the human
race AND appreciate food. Afterwards we went for a walk on
the downs; while Erasmus and I held hands she told us about
her good works in Southwark. Some of the boys in the
Southwark slum she'd known all their lives, and they still kept
in touch with her now that they were grown up men with boys
of their own. As I listened to her witty stories which were
always free of malice, I thought how different she was from
Nora. Nora wouldn't be talking about people on this walk –
she'd be drawing our attention to the flowers that grow on
chalk and the butterflies they attract.

Helen devoted most of her time to her father. The diaries
she kept during their trips abroad read like a Baedeker. When
she came with us to France she knew exactly where there was
anything worthwhile to see, from a cathedral in a city square
to a small romanesque church tucked away off the main
road.

But that belonged to the future, forty years later when she
was old, lame and almost blind in one eye; on this memorable
June the first, she was not only spry mentally, something she
was never to lose, but spry physically as well. All her
movements had a gusto as though there was plenty of energy
to spare. Tea poured, bread cut, butter spread, home-made
jam released from its jar, all done with the virgin strength that
only a spinster, untramelled by family life, can have.

We drove home through the bean flower scent with a sense
of well-being I shall never forget. Erasmus told me he had got
tickets for the May week Ball assuming I would be able to
accept. I did. My happiness was almost complete, but not
quite, because I wanted him to ask me to marry him. I wanted
quite desperately to say 'yes'. The stars came out, the moon
shone brightly and my parents obliged by not waking up
when we let ourselves into the house. We sat down on the sofa

and talked about the future with no reference to the past. Erasmus said the future without me looked very, very bleak. I waited and then prompted, Is that a proposal?" and it was *he* who answered 'yes'.

Erasmus and I were now engaged but no-one was to know. My mother, after the previous hullabaloo, had fixed up for me to go to Heidelburg expressly to avoid what she now called 'nonsense like that again'. My father must have peace to write and with me being hysterical how could he hope to work? She insisted I had six weeks without seeing Erasmus before I made up my mind. A six week break with a family in Germany where there was a son a few years older than I. I explained all this to Erasmus and swore him to silence. A secret engagement was romantic. I propped Erasmus's photograph up on the mantleshelf in my bedroom and kissed it before I went to sleep. This was something I could keep to myself. Something of my very own. Something I thought no one could spoil, until the end of that week when my father came into the room with a letter in his hand. He was smiling against his will, as though he knew he should be looking severe.

'Alan Barlow tells me you and Erasmus are engaged,' he said, 'why didn't you tell me yourself? You're not yet nineteen, under age, I could say 'no' then you'll have to wait until you are twenty-one but I won't. . .' he paused and unable to conceal the pleasure he felt gave up the heavy father act and took me in his arms. 'I'm glad. I always preferred Erasmus to all your other young men. But your mother won't be all that pleased I'm afraid.'

I let him kiss me and then, fearing a sentimental scene, wriggled out of his embrace. Erasmus had not only told his parents, but all his friends had been informed too. He had been unable to keep the news to himself. Some of the response to the news had undertones I didn't like, Denis Ewer wrote:

Dear Biddy,
    I learned this evening this charming news about your successes in the market.
    As one who knows your man for many years permit me to say that your fishing is as skilled as that of the Premier and your catch as delectable (and gentlemanly) as the

Foreign Secretary.

I hope (even be it at Gretna Green) you will not forget to invite me to your final linking, the more I may send you one of those attractive glass jerries (I have however learned that the man considers the law, at any rate, will not consume the matter for another three years) that is my common practice to send people in your condition.

To make the matter the more charming, the good gentleman here assembled have agreed to subscribe their names.

> Jakes Ewer
> (no, sorry Denis)
> Mark Pryor
> John Humphrey
> David Webb

Hugh Gordon wrote in a similar vein, wishing Erasmus the best of luck with the Irish temperament. Nora, wanting to sound pleased yet unable to compromise the truth, took refuge in platitudes:

Dear Biddy,

I am glad that the peace of decision has descended on you both. It is the beginning of a new chapter, which ought to be one of the best – so here's my blessing, and may the chapter have the peace of real understanding till the end.

Yours

N.B.

My parents were invited to Boswells to discuss the engagement and now my father, the only one who had been really enthusiastic, began to grumble.

'If Alan Barlow expects a marriage settlement I shall have to tell him there isn't an earthly hope.'

He need not have worried. A dowry was never mentioned, although, oddly enough, a divorce settlement somehow crept into the conversation, but my mother quashed that one straight away – such financial security might break up a marriage rather than help it to survive.

What were we going to live on when we got married? Alan
asked. He had suffered Erasmus's political opinion long
enough and now, at last, he had a chance to fight back. Erasmus was a member of the Communist Party – how was he
going to square that with getting married on a private income?
My parents were nonplussed and Nora by suggesting a long
engagement somehow managed to convey that that might
solve the problem because our love would be unlikely to survive the test of time. She doubted if our temperaments
were suited,

'Erasmus is so drab, and Biddy is so lively', which my
mother interpreted as:

'My sensible son is far too good for your flibbertigibbet
daughter.' They criticised Erasmus's extravagant nature. He
was such a contrast to his brother Andrew, who was prudent
to the extreme about money.

'If I told Erasmus and Andrew to go and buy a dressing-
gown,' Alan Barlow said, 'Erasmus would choose the most
expensive camel hair one and Andrew come back with an old
sack in which he had cut two holes for his arms.'

Divorce, marriage, engagement, politics and money. I took
it all in at one gulp and digested it slowly bit by bit. Erasmus's
private income, however small, seemed adequate – almost
luxurious, because it was there, willy-nilly, unlike my father's
income which had to be earned with hours and hours of
thinking up plots and shaping them into a story, not knowing
whether the result would be acceptable to an editor or not. If
Erasmus's political ideals clashed with such a supreme bonus
as a private income then they were doubly silly. I had no
political conscience and very few ideals. I was determined on
one thing now that Erasmus and I were engaged. We would
wait a year before getting married, but why wait any longer? I
was not going to interfere with Erasmus's career. I was going
to help him to work.

Erasmus had tickets for the May Week Ball and at last what
had been a vague promise for many years had become a
reality. Lady Darwin invited me to stay at The Orchard and
knowing this time what to expect, I packed my clothes between layers of tissue paper. I even bought a sponge bag, but I
still lacked slippers and dressing-gown. For those essentials I
had to wait to be a fully fledged Barlow.

In the afternoon we went through the conventional ritual of choosing the engagement ring. Erasmus took me to a jeweller in the Market Square where a whole tray of glittering stones was displayed in front of me. Intimidated by the prices which would conflict with Erasmus's political ideals, and make inroads into his private income, I chose the cheapest – three pounds worth of minute opals set between pin heads of shiny glass in eight carat gold. It fitted exactly, an excellent omen, I was sure.

We were a large party going to the ball and before setting out, the young ladies paraded before Lady Darwin and her daughter Ruth. My dress of peach-coloured tulle with roses round the bodice had been designed by myself and run up by the village dressmaker. It received much praise, but the ring on my fourth finger which I was more eager to show off than my dress was dismissed by Lady Darwin as a 'nice little ring', as though it was a trinket that had fallen out of a cracker. Ruth Darwin obviously felt the same although she tried to appear enthusiastic. My mother, the most unworldly of women, also surprised me with her reaction when I showed her my ring. She sighed, shook her head and hinted I deserved something better, as though the cheapness of the ring undervalued her daughter. I didn't care. For me that ring was perfect. It had been chosen by Erasmus and myself and symbolised the love we felt for each other.

We spent most of the time of the May Week Ball in Erasmus's rooms, which were close to the large marquee where the band played much too loudly and my toes suffered when we danced. Dawn seeped through the darkness and we watched the sun rise on Trinity Bridge until the last waltz when Erasmus and I, in a tight clinch, gyrated on the floor, and then stood in sulky silence while the National Anthem was played.

It was morning, sunny and warm, and the fun wasn't over yet. We all piled into cars – yes, 'piled into cars' – that was the expression used for the post-ball drive out to Barton Mills for a swim in the river. Embarrassed by the lack of cover I could not bring myself to change into my bathing costume and feigning the time-of-the-month excuse, I stood on the bank in my peach-coloured gown watching the others splash around in the water. Breakfast at the Bull Hotel with our boisterous laughter attracting the attention of other guests. Unaccustomed to university life they thought the sight of us in evening dress consuming bacon and eggs most eccentric, when in fact it was the conventional thing to do.

When we got back to The Orchard, Lady Darwin insisted I should rest. A maid tucked me up in bed but I could not sleep; as soon as I drifted off I woke with a jolt and held out my left hand towards the curtained light to make sure that my engagement ring was still on.

There was a party in Erasmus's rooms where a never-ending stream of young men came through the door. They were mostly the pastel tie brigade with keen intelligent faces and strong views. I had already met Martin Pollock, John Kidd and Mark Pryor but here were hundreds more. How could anyone have so many friends? With such a number would I ever be able to call Erasmus my own?

Overwhelmed by what I now recognise as the other-people's-friends syndrome, I was glad to escape to Harlton and be reassured by the familiar Darwin smell and striped curtains when we had tea with Gwen Raverat. Here was a house where people did things with not too much fuss about clearing up and leaving everything tidy. In the sitting-room Gwen engraved her wood cuts on a large table and there was a press for making trial prints on one side.

There was a piano littered with music. Elisabeth sang and Sophie played the violin. Both Gwen's daughters could paint and draw. They also made their own clothes. I could have been daunted by so much talent, but these beautiful, gifted girls also had social grace and knew how to put me at my ease. Gwen seemed to take very little notice of me or anyone else; only later was I to discover that in spite of her abstracted manner she was very much aware of everything that was happening around her. One meeting with me would be enough for her to sum up my character and that summing up would carry great weight with the rest of the family. Many, many times I heard Gwen quoted and watched opinions swayed by her judgement. 'Gwen said. . .' could put the seal of approval of the weight of condemnation on someone like myself.

5

Erasmus and I were officially engaged but it was decided that no announcement should be made in the paper until nearer the date. We were engaged, yet we weren't really engaged. We were going to get married but that was not definite, either. It was an unsatisfactory cloud-cuckoo land in which to live; plans were made but they were unreal plans, more like dreams, and decisions lacked substance.

Erasmus had to have somewhere to live in London now that he was to be a medical student at University College Hospital. John Humphrey and Martin Pollock had already settled in Great James Street in Bloomsbury and he automatically gravitated there since it would be nice to be near his friends and within walking distance of the hospital. Perhaps I was consulted about our future home, but I don't remember seeing any flats until the choice had been made. This was where I should return after our honeymoon. That honeymoon was shrouded in the mists of unreality so why take seriously the dark entrance to our flat with the smell of cat impregnated linoleum, the long climb up the dusty staircase to the narrow landing and 'our' front door with the Yale lock as somewhere I was going to live?

The furniture arrived but I had no hand in choosing it. Ruth Darwin, Helen Barlow and Nora all contributed pieces of solid mahogany and sensible oak which were perhaps more blessed to give than to receive into a small flat. Nora was willing to arrange these family rejects in the three rooms which were to be decorated when colour schemes had been agreed upon. I went off to Germany knowing that by the time I returned everything to do with the flat would have been settled.

Heidelburg with its fairytale castle, its terraces, the slow-moving river could not have been more different from the

64

suburb of Cologne where I had spent the summer last year.
And the lively family always breaking into song, even over the
washing-up, also contrasted with the sad Mullers. The Panzers
were friendly and warm. They reminded me of my own family
with their high spirits and arguments at meals, but there was
one huge difference which my parents can't have known.
They were Nazis. Dedicated Nazis. The house was festooned
with flags. Swastikas flapped in the breeze, a life-size picture
of Hitler hung on the wall. His eyes were supposed to follow
wherever one went in the room. There was a printed form
stuck to the inside of the front door. The air raid precautions.
Marianne, the eldest daughter, was named as the warden. She
would be the one with the whistle who was responsible for
directing the family to the shelter. It was all planned, as
though war was was not only inevitable but might break out
next week.

Actually war did not break out next week, instead Erasmus
arrived hot foot from England. The Panzers offered him a bed
in one of their many rooms and we spent days wandering in
the woods discussing the decorating of the flat. Nora's choice
of bluey-grey clashed with my craving for pink. On a sandy
track between the pine trees I stopped and scraping the
ground with my foot said, 'That is the colour I want.' I really
felt quite strongly about that dusty pink but at such a distance
my opinion had little chance of winning against the sensible
bluey-grey.

After Erasmus went back, Frau Panzer gave her son
Siegfried the job of entertaining me. He showed me the town,
we walked down flagstone streets, admired old houses with
window boxes full of geraniums, and drank coffee at a cafe
table on the pavement while we talked. We went to a concert in
the castle and with our elbows touching enjoyed an intermin-
able Bruckner symphony. The weather was sunny and warm,
we had every excuse to escape from the house and bicycle
further up the river to swim. We lay in the grass and discussed
marriage in a general way until Siegfried became more
specific. He asked me if I thought a mixed marriage would
work. A German boy marrying an English girl? I answered
'no' and when asked why such a definite 'no' I began quite
gently to explain our political differences, which somehow
became personal and abusive. I ended up having to apologise

for what I had said.

'I can forgive, but I can never forget,' Siegfried replied, and went into a decline. His parents decided he needed mountain air to restore his spirits and sent him away to the Bavarian Alps. A timely piece of parental interference enabling me to return to England having passed the test of separation from Erasmus. Just.

Years later, in the tidy way that life sometimes has, Erasmus and I and our three children found ourselves in Heidelburg again. On the spur of the moment we decided to go and look at the house where we had stayed. Across the bridge, turn left, and there, overlooking the slow moving Neckar it stood, unscarred by war but no longer bedecked with swastikas. We rang the front door-bell, curious to know what had happened to this Nazi family. We were prepared for the shock of hearing they were all dead, but totally unprepared for the shock of hearing they were all very much alive. All of them, right now, were out in the garden celebrating the Herr Professors's 80th birthday!

A smiling Siegfried introduced me to his wife, and I thought uncharitably what a dumpy little *Hausfrau* he had married. We all sat down to tea and discussed the war. They, like all good Nazis, had seen the error of their ways, except Marianne, who couldn't bring herself to deny her loyalty to Hitler. 'It's too soon,' she kept saying, 'too soon.' Siegfried at a riper age was no more sensible than he had been as a young man. There was an overloaded handshake, a significant kiss, deep lingering look from eyes glazed with tears, which all goes to prove what I've suspected for many years – one gets more silly, not less with the passing of the years.

When I got off the train at Victoria station and saw Erasmus waiting for me on the platform I dropped my heavy suitcase and bolted into his arms. While staying with the Panzers I had the unpleasant sensation that my molecules had been thrown into disarray but now I felt all of a piece again. It would have been different had the Panzers been horrible, which would have been in keeping with their thoroughly nasty politics, but they weren't horrible, they were absolutely charming, and it was this inconsistency that produced the conflict, compounded of course by Siegfried, who always seemed to be lurking behind doors ready to pounce out on me. I tried to explain all this to Erasmus as we drove home in the car but I doubt if he understood my garbled account because I evaded telling the whole truth, feeling that the whole truth wasn't mine to tell.

Within a few days of getting home I was packing my suitcase again in preparation for going to Ireland with the Barlows. How Erasmus had fixed that I should tag along too I shall never know. Nora probably guessed he would have refused to have gone if I wasn't included, and she wanted all her children there because this was the last chance of a family holiday together. Thomas was being posted abroad for two years.

We went in two cars and I, having filled my case with clothes, emptied an armful of shoes into the back of the one that Erasmus drove. When Nora found she had nowhere to put her feet except on top of my shoes she felt obliged to say,

'Just as well we don't all travel with our shoes like this.' Although it was said nicely, and everyone laughed, I was suddenly aware that I was no longer just 'a charming girl from a crazy Irish family', but a trainee in becoming a Barlow. That didn't stop me from making further mistakes.

I fussed about what I ate before going on the boat and when the wind whipped up and the sea became very rough, so rough that even Nora, the most unneurotic traveller, confessed to feeling claustrophobic in her small cabin, I fussed about being sick. I fussed about my lack of sleep and although I didn't actually voice a fuss about bathing in the nude I was obviously so embarrassed when the whole family stripped off in a lonely cove that Nora took me further up the beach to swim in privacy without our costumes. She had pandered to my prudish behaviour although she disapproved of it. For her, nudity was the norm. 'There's nothing so horrible as peeping,' she once said. If 'horrible' was a synonym for 'sexy' then what she was saying fitted very well with Robin Pearce's philosophy about keeping on one's clothes when making love.

Our destination was Achill Island where we occupied the entire hotel. We were a party of nine and each day we all did something together. We walked, bathed, went to the races, all of us together. Never any rows, never any arguments, never any rush of uncontrollable high spirits. Nora, calm and smiling, organised each day and Alan, in his own quiet fashion apparently enjoyed the rare proximity with his family. He never contributed much to any outing, he just came along; if there was an opportunity to communicate he quickly hid behind *The Times* and concentrated on the crossword which he completed in record time.

Erasmus and I tended to cut ourselves off from the rest of the family. On walks we either dropped behind or strode quickly ahead. I remember puffing our way up a mountain and getting into a heated argument over the subject of putting young children into crèches. Erasmus, still spellbound by what he had seen in the Soviet Union, was tremendously in favour of women having jobs and letting someone else have the responsibility of bringing up the children – which I was very much against.

When I was young I had been taken by an aunt to a crèche in the East End of London. It was a very hot day and the smell of disinfectant combined with the sound of crying children left an indelible impression which I recalled as I stumped along beside Erasmus up the mountain. I could not reconcile loving him and despising his opinions; when he mentioned birth control, which somehow followed on from the crèche controversy I was angry and disgusted. On another occasion I was reduced to tears by what I considered to be his inconsiderate behaviour. In a thick mist we were scrambling up a cliff. It was tricky rather than dangerous, but nevertheless I felt Erasmus should have been at my side instead of forging ahead not even looking round to see if I was all right and leaving Thomas to give me the helping hand. In the evening these little differences were patched up after a few minutes alone together. Erasmus always volunteered to put the cars away in the garage and I always went with him. In the dark, ignoring the discomfort of the cramped front seat, we managed to embrace in spite of the steering wheel and gears which like chaperones ensured we never got too close.

The time we spent putting the cars away was often disproportionately long, and when we returned to the sitting room, flushed and rumpled, the atmosphere was tense beneath the apparent calm of Alan filling in the crossword puzzle and the staccato click click of Nora's knitting needles. Towards the end of the fortnight my precarious mood stabilised and in a lucid interval I realised how selfish my behaviour had been. I reviled myself for not having mixed in more with the family instead of seeking Erasmus's company alone. In our exclusive preference for each other we had added very little to the holiday. As a last minute attempt to make amends, I did everything I could to wipe out the bad impression I must have made. I played cards with Joan, built sandcastles with Horace, plunged into the chilly sea with Hilda and suggested games we could all join in while Erasmus went alone to put the cars away in the garage. These last few days of the holiday were the most enjoyable.

Before we went to Ireland my father, knowing we were going to pass through Sligo on our way back from Achill Island, dictated to his secretary a list of all my relatives' names, occupations and where their bones lay buried in that county. They were doctors, lawyers, clergymen, not of *The Origin of Species* class, just ordinary people whose memory my father cherished. Nora was rather amused by what my father had done but the names of so many relations, not one of whom had contributed anything significant to history, failed to arouse sufficient interest to warrant stopping the car. Although I knew what pleasure my father would get from hearing we had visited the grave of my great grandfather I didn't like to press the point, especially as it would have meant traipsing around a churchyard in the rain.

On our journey home through England we called in at the Wedgwood factory in Barlaston and after a minimum of name dropping some pinstriped official gave us a guided tour of the works. Thomas, to my surprise, talked about our wedding as though it was really going to happen and not a game of make-believe. He regretted he would be away for what he described as 'the great day' and would like, since we were in the factory, to take the opportunity of giving us a wedding present now. Quite a little speech he made, a trifle stuffy but very, very sweet. We were told to take our choice. I had no idea what we wanted and with such a bewildering display of beautiful things, so many plates, cups, vases and jugs I was too bemused to speak. Mercifully Erasmus spotted something he liked. A black coffee set. He held up one of the cups for me to see how the shiny interior contrasted with the lack lustre outside. Nora tentatively suggested the black coffee might lose its identity in the black cups, but Erasmus had made up his mind and no argument would persuade him that the black coffee set, twelve cups, elegant pot and sugar basin, was not just what we needed in the Great James Street flat. Thomas wrote out a cheque and it was agreed that our first wedding present should be sent to Boswells, where it remained for eight years without being unpacked.

We visited Lichfield, the birth place of Erasmus Darwin, who was Nora'a great great grandfather and Erasmus's namesake. Nora told me that this ancestor had invented a vertical windmill, written an enlightened book on female education and developed his own theory of evolution long before his son Charles came up with the one that shook the world. I wasn't particularly interested in what she said but I listened politely, while wondering why this fat old gentleman, stuck high up on the family tree, belonging to the past, had anything to do with the present which concerned Erasmus and me.

We dropped Hilda off at a dingy railway station, in the middle of nowhere, and she was left in a chilly waiting-room to revise for her exams until the train came in two hours' time to take her to where she had to go. It seemed a very bleak end to a holiday. My parents under such circumstances would never have treated me like that – there would have been a splendid send-off with hugs and kisses and waving on the platform until the train was out of sight. But the Barlows had a spartan streak which didn't include self-denial of food. I'd been astonished on this holiday by their arguments over the last helping of treacle pudding or who was entitled to the lone potato left in the dish. It takes all sorts of families to make in-laws; not a very profound observation, perhaps, but a lesson I learned with some misgiving, which explains, dear Freud, the loss of my engagement ring on our way home. But that doesn't explain why I found it again, unless you believe in the intervention of Saint Anthony, who in a demanding schedule managed to keep guard in the café cloakroom until after driving many miles down the road, we returned to find my precious ring, exactly where I left it, on the edge of the wash basin, the imitation diamonds twinkling with pleasure at seeing me again. Actually it was myself doing the twinkling when I should have been offering grateful thanks with prayers and lighted candles to this overworked saint.

At home a letter from Siegfried awaited me. It began 'how is *mein Bidlein*' and went on with some jolly banter and rather clever illustrations of what he'd been doing since I'd left Germany. Momentarily I was filled with a restless nostalgia for my time in Heidelberg; the days there seemed carefree and sun-lit compared to the well-structured rainy holiday with the Barlows in Ireland.

Before my engagement to Erasmus our two families seemed very much the same. We enjoyed doing similar things and held more or less identical political views, yet, for some reason now, the fractional differences outweighed the common denominator, as though it was easier to be a friend of the Barlows than a prospective daughter-in-law.

I began to feel like a skin graft about to be rejected by its host when Nora gently drew attention to the way I drank my soup.

'What a funny way you hold your spoon,' she remarked, 'and wouldn't it be better if you tipped your plate away from you as I do.' Her advice on how to behave towards the servants was like an extract from a book on etiquette. They must be noticed, even if they were busily occupied doing something else, redistributing the dust, for instance, and showing no inclination to notice me. I must learn to say 'good morning' or 'good evening' or whatever time of day it was to a fleeting back or a humped bottom sweeping the stairs.

'They'll never respect you but at least you can get them to like you,' I was told. She spoke with the force of a convert who once had found it difficult to practise what she now preached. As a young girl she had gone to extraordinary lengths to avoid the obligatory greeting – taking a circuitous route through the garden so as not to meet the gardener and staying inside her bedroom until the cleaning had stopped outside the door.

In September Erasmus installed himself in the flat and started work at University College Hospital where most of his friends from Cambridge had elected to go. Relations who visited the flat were very outspoken about its inconvenience. Ruth Darwin criticised the washing facilities – most unhygienic to have a lavatory in the kitchen, and a plywood screen around it was quite inadequate, against the L.C.C. regulations, she was sure. And where was I going to wash my face? In the sink where the washing-up was done? Yes, where else?

And how was I going to prepare food without a kitchen table? But there was a kitchen table, or rather a wooden surface that had to be pulled down over the bath. What a pity the taps got so greasy from frying on the gas stove. Helen Barlow worried about the size of the bedroom. With two beds, next to each other, there was no space left on either side and we would have to walk up the beds to get under the covers. I listened to their criticisms and denied anything was wrong. We were marrying young before Erasmus was earning. 'We're lucky to have any-where,' I said, and thought, Oh hell, they're right, they're horribly right, damn them all.

Slowly it dawned on me that I was considered more a poten-tial liability for Erasmus than a bonus which migh enhance the quality of his life. His work had already suffered through me – the emotional upheaval I had caused over our engage-ment had resulted in his disappointing degree; now it was essential no demands were made on him and he was allowed to get on with his career. Nora talked about Emma Darwin who had been such a strength and support to her famous hus-band, never interfering with the hours he spent on research. Erasmus had already decided research was what he wanted to do and I was fully prepared to slip into the back seat role of the good little woman helping her man by being absolutely noth-ing, until Martin Pollock, who lived in the flat below, told me what Erasmus did when he returned from the hospital in the evening.

'He's always trying out some new recipe,' he complained, 'or cleaning out the fridge. He is obviously happier in the kitchen than he is studying, but he'll never pass his exams that way.'

How Erasmus spent his evenings was beyond my control but I felt responsible nevertheless and came to the conclusion that the only way to get him away from the kitchen and back to his desk was to beat him at his own game and become an effi-cient cook myself. I joined a cookery class at the Chelsea Polytechnic and went there three mornings a week to master the basic principals of preparing a meal. A large proportion of debutantes attended the class and they, unlike myself, took their lessons very lightly. They were filling in time rather than mastering a skill and were often too enthralled with discussing last night's ball to notice what they were doing. Sometimes they turned off the wrong gas jet with dire consequence if it was my lovingly prepared dish that they spoiled. Proudly I presented Erasmus with my trophies and watched him wolf down in a few minutes what had taken me a whole morning to prepare. Some of the rules that I learned then I still practice now: always use a metal spoon rather than a wooden one for scrambling eggs; let the browned flour cool in the meat pan before pouring in the stock; and to prevent a white sauce becoming lumpy add boiling milk to the roux paste. Such relatively unimportant bits of knowledge gave me confidence to assert my right to be in the kitchen if and when my presence there was disputed.

My studies, now overshadowed by Erasmus's career, became less important, and my mother, ever fearful of me breaking down under strain, suggested I should switch from the arduous degree course to a much less demanding diploma, one which would leave time for the wedding pre-parations even if the wedding would not take place. It also meant I could live at home, away from the temptations of Erasmus's flat, a far more important consideration in her eyes, I am sure. Nora approved and the director of studies readily agreed when I explained to him, with much twiddling of my engagement ring, that I was going to be married at the end of the academic year.

Students on the psychology diploma course were housed in cramped quarters at the top of the zoology department. We were definitely second class citizens, kept far away from the intellectual whirl of the rest of University College. Lectures were sparse, and no-one seemed to care whether any written work was done. We spent a lot of time doing rather futile experiments which involved sitting in a darkened room and dabbing each other with powder puffs, and writing down our introspections afterwards.

We worked together in pairs, and my partner was Roy Lewis, who like many others on the course left before taking the diploma. Years later when we me again he was African cor respondent for *The Times*.

'Are you the girl who blushed at Flugel's lecture on the Freudian interpretation of the smoke-room joke?' he asked, and I had to admit to being the blushing prude. I should have saved my blushes for Cyril Burt. He taught us how to test intelligence using methods that produced results which have since fallen into disrepute. I don't know how he did this, some kind of skullduggery which showed at any rate there was nothing wrong with his IQ.

Erasmus and I often met for lunch. He was just the other side of the road from University College, and the medical school refectory provided cheap and almost edible food.

The doctors sat together at the end of the long room. I naturally revered them. They were superior beings – Ashley Miles, grey haired and very handsome; Harry Himsworth, distinguished in his green tweed suit; and Thomas Lewis with such a brazen stare that I asked Erasmus,

'Who is that old boy with bright blue eyes who keeps ogling me?'

We rarely ate alone as one of Erasmus's many friends would drift in through the swing doors and ask to join us. Philip Gell, John Humphrey, Heinz Wolff, Martin Pollock. . . The better I got to know them the more I liked them, and it is one of my real joys that they are still our friends today.

And then there were the relations who as Erasmus's fiancée I now met. Not many on the Barlow side but a confusion of cousins on Nora's. Cornfords, Keynes, Raverats, even if they had changed their surnames through marriage they retained their genetic birthright.

Billy and Mona Darwin invited us to a sherry party in a house facing Regent's Park. Mona was extremely elegant. She wore haute couture garnished with pearls, diamonds and scarlet nail varnish. The broad, white streak in her jet black hair was proof according to Nora, though I can't think why, that this Darwin rebel had had her hair dyed – a rather wicked thing to do. Furthermore Billy, brave man, was a successful stockbroker, unashamedly rich. Besides being Mona's husband he was Gwen Raverat's, and Margaret Keynes' brother.

They gave us a warm welcome as though we were very special guests and told their two sons in dark suits to ply us with food and drink. For me one glass of sherry was one glass too many and with flushed cheeks I talked to the nodding head of a music critic about Percy Grainger. Very gratifying at the time but devastating once I had sobered up and realised that while I had been holding forth so knowledgeably about Percy Grainger I had meant to be talking about Peter Warlock.

Under the influence of drink, I muddled up their names.

There was a dinner party at the Keynes, who lived in a huge house in Arkwright Road. The bedrooms were all named after Downe House, where Charles Darwin wrote *The Origin of Species* – so I was told by Margaret who took me upstairs to leave my coat and my hat in Sand Walk. At dinner the four sons sat in a row facing Erasmus and myself. Their grey flannel suits and neatly knotted school ties made a great impression on me. Richard, handsome and silent; Quentin, a romantic figure recovering from polio; Milo, a mini Goering with an array of badges across his chest, and Stephen, all sparkle and lively charm. Geoffrey, at the head of the table, seemed on edge, as though the effort of being *en famille* was too much for him, and Margaret's determination to put us at our ease was counter-productive. When Erasmus went silent I threw myself conversationally at the four sons, treating them as though they were children to be charmed, not yet realising that charm was suspect in a Darwin's eyes.

Eventually the dinner ground to its end. I had done my best. I had even filled in an awkward silence by mentioning my grandmother whom I only recall meeting once in my life, but now was someone with whom it was convenient to claim a closer aquaintanceship, because she, too, had lived in Arkwright Road.

'One of the houses near the bottom of the hill,' I explained. No reaction. 'She was nearly blind,' I continued, but that generated no interest either. 'There was a cuckoo clock in the hall – we have it now, only it doesn't always work – the cuckoo sounds the wrong hour.' The boys looked blank, Margaret gave a nervous cough, and Geoffrey having fetched the port from the sideboard handed me the decanter. 'Help yourself,' he said. It was a command, not a request, and having taken a minimum dose I handed the bottle back to him. This lack of know-how produced the only animated moment of the evening. My simple action was greeted with screams of 'widdershins' and Geoffrey, voluble at last, explained the social blunder I had committed by passing the ruddy port the wrong way round the table.

Once we had escaped from the large red brick ugly house, Erasmus was prepared to talk. I had plenty to say, too.

'I felt I ought to cross myself every time Charles Darwin was mentioned,' I exclaimed,' and why did they always refer to him as CD?'

'Those are his initials,' replied Erasmus, as if I didn't know.

'Family pride is like patriotism – alright in small doses but harmful in excess. Fancy naming rooms after C.D.'s house,' the initials turned into a sneer, 'and even the dog in your family can't be given a normal name. Why is it called Gene instead of Jean I'd like to know.'

'Mama got her from Fisher's Genetic Research Institute, because of that Gene seemed rather a suitable name.'

'Well I think it's ridiculous and the sooner you forget your famous ancestry and settle for just being ordinary the better for everyone.'

'Perhaps you should join in the anti-Darwin league. Mona started it when she married Billy.'

'Why did she bother to do that?'

'I suppose she felt swamped by them all, not coming from a very distinguished family herself.'

I ground my teeth with suppressed irritation until the silence between us cracked.

'I'm not going to join the anti-Darwin league,' I said, 'if I did, that would give them more importance than they warrant. Look how much stronger the Fascists have become since the anti-Fascists were formed.'

'The Darwins aren't Fascists,' Erasmus replied perhaps missing the point in order to put an end to my diatribe.

Let it be recorded now that Hilda, on a least one occasion, denied herself a boost by refusing to mention Charles Darwin. A fellow student asked the name of her famous relation. 'You must mean Billy Darwin,' replied Hilda, 'he's my stockbroker uncle.'

When Nora asked me about our dinner at Arkwright Road I gave a carefully edited account, not wanting her to know the exasperation I had felt, but somehow she guessed that the evening with the Keynes had not been a great success and to my surprise seemed pleased that it should have been so.

'Geoffrey is so terribly vain,' she said, 'and Margaret, well. . .' She gave a deprecating laugh which expressed her feelings towards the youngest member of her closely knit Darwin clan.

'We always looked upon her as a bit of a joke, partly because of the things she said. So naive. The trouble is she never seems to have grown up.'

Christopher, the son of Frances Cornford, expressed a similar sentiment in a speech he made at Margaret's seventieth birthday celebration; only he was paying her a very great compliment when he said,

'Margaret will always be nine years old.' And I think it is true to say that that wide-eyed innocence of such a golden age remained with her until she died. She was a very sweet person. Perhaps not appreciated by her cousins, certainly not appreciated by me in the throes of inlaw-itis.

6

It was not long before I discovered the magical effect the name Darwin could have and I regret to say I fell prey to using it when necessary myself. Doors were opened where they had been closed before and bored expressions lightened with keen interest when I revealed my tenuous link with this family who often seemed rather dull in a stodgy, monosyllabic way. The other side of the coin to this card of access was the high standard that was expected in any achievement. In my family a success, however small, was acclaimed with a fanfare of amazed delight, but in the Barlow-Darwins it was the *Origin of Species* or bust! When Erasmus got six credits in his school certificate, which was far better than he had ever hoped, the news was received with coolness as if that was the least one should expect, and nothing whatsoever to celebrate.

When people expressed envy at my marrying into such an interesting family I found it more and more difficult to know what to reply. One very distinguished relative and many descendants do not make an interesting person. Even someone talking about an interesting subject can be boring if the tone of voice is monotonous and there are no gaps left in the account for comments from anybody else. And there is nothing more deadly than those who take such a pride in their genes that they feel they can lie back and enjoy their inheritance without making an effort to communicate.

I began to dread those social occasions when inevitably the Darwin family tree insinuated its roots into the conversation. As Erasmus gave the details I, already bored by this subject, would begin to fidget, perhaps raise my eyes to heaven while unsuccessfully repressing a sigh. A host, more sensitive than the average, who invited us out to dinner during the first months of our engagement, noticed my reaction to the topic which made Erasmus suddenly blossom, and decided Erasmus's family should not be allowed to monopolise the conversation. With a smile of feigned interest he turned to me and asked,

'Your father was part of the Sexton Blake team, wasn't he? How absolutely fascinating that must have been.' He meant well, but oh dear. . . . His good intentions had one result. I vowed that from then on I would hide my irritation, perhaps even manage a smile, when the talk turned to the Darwin ancestry.

I was proud of my own family but not because of what they had achieved, which did not amount to very much, but because of what they were – lively, charming and good-looking.

It took me several months to find out that Erasmus's pride in his family was in a different class from mine. The discovery could well have been delayed if my mother hadn't decided to talk about the future. Had I really thought about it? She asked. Irritated by her worried expression and serious voice I demanded to know exactly what she meant by the question. Babies. Of course we were going to have a family. That was the whole point of getting married, surely? No, I was not going to discuss birth control. A revolting subject. Taboo. I started to cry. My mother became more distressed. When she mentioned one or two methods I blocked my ears and ran from the room. She followed me out into the garden where a tact-less thrush was advocating careless rapture from the top of a tree. Since I refused to discuss what she called 'the necessary evil' she began to talk about her own fears: could a hare lip and cleft palate be inherited? Did I really want to marry into a family if there was a chance of this deformity appearing again? I had no idea. Such a thought had never entered my head. My mother persisted. Perhaps I should think about it seriously. Ask Erasmus. His feelings might be hurt, but ask him I must. I plucked up courage and introduced the subject as tactfully as I could. Erasmus's reaction astonished me. With every birth there was a risk of deformity, he said, and quoted statistics from an article in *The Lancet* to prove his point. But with that risk, in his family, came the chance, the golden chance, of inheriting some of the genius genes. Charles Darwin was his great, great grandfather! 'Oh calumniating time,' it wasn't as bad as that, was it?

My mother had never been very much in favour of my engagement to Erasmus; although she had not actually voiced her fears until now I had always been aware of a certain reluctance to share the enthusiasm which my father felt. With hindsight I think this was probably due to a number of reasons rather than a single cause. My immaturity was an adequate peg on which to hang any amount of worry and was completely justified. Less justified was the worry that the Barlows would expect a grander wedding than we could afford. She didn't know of Nora's deep rooted desire for simplicity, the 'that will do' attitude which was clearly expressed in a letter to Erasmus:

> 'Gwen was reminding me that Helena's wedding, which she ran at Harlton, was described as such a nice amateurish sort of wedding, so I think we shall be in that category too, and much the nicest.'

Nora shied away from formality; she had been married in a coat and skirt – not a new coat and skirt, but one she had been wearing every day for many years. She told me it was purple.

I fussed about my trousseau, nagged my poor parents, convinced that it would never materialise unless I kept on at them as the weeks passed by. Eventually my mother went into action on my behalf and directed an ex-nun living in Kent to hand-stitch three sets of underwear from the lengths of silk, satin and crepe de chine which had been bought as remnants during the sales. The ex-nun duly did as she was told – scalloping, hem stiching, embroidering wherever she could, perhaps longing as I did for a little excitement with a piece of ruched lace, but lace my mother forbade. I wrote to Erasmus that my trousseau was lovely, but there were no 'thrills' – a Freudian slip for the forbidden frills.

The problems of 'the bridal gown' was solved by my godmother who sent a length of Liberty brocade which was not white for this very white wedding but a pale mushroom pink shot with silver flowers. Since Nora had spurned conventional attire for her own wedding there was no veil stored away in tissue paper and of course nothing like that had survived in my family. I would have to make do with plain tulle. Nora's idea, and she promised a wreath of roses from the Boswells' garden to keep it in place.

The bridesmaids were to carry bunches of sweet peas which

matched their multi-coloured chiffon dresses. No-one thought about what should be worn underneath this clinging material and there is a photograph of Gill, Hilda and Sophie standing in a row with a breeze blowing their skirts against their legs, revealing different styles of knickers!

Plans and more plans. Attention to detail was sporadic. Wedding invitations had priority. No silver bells for me instead, with an enormous amount of organisation they had to be specially designed and printed in Eric Gill type by a rarified young man in High Wycombe. Very nice they looked, but with so much going on I wonder how my father had time to fuss about such a relatively trivial detail.

Decisions were somehow reached by a small committee consisting mainly of Nora and anyone else who happened to be around at that moment. I had a few concrete opinions myself and was always pleased with the result, thankful to have one more obstacle out of the way. However, when it came to the music for my wedding I really felt I had a right to be consulted, and Nora, myself, Erasmus, Elisabeth Raverat, Joan and several others, all met at Yarners, the coffee house next to the Queen's Hall in order to draw up a programme as if for a concert rather than an order of service for two people being married.

Elisabeth had a lovely rich, brown contralto voice and I was delighted that she should sing during the signing in the vestry. But what was she to sing? Different opinions were voiced but no-one asked my opinion until Elisabeth said, 'What would Biddy like?' My reply: Handel's 'Trust in the Lord' was quickly dismissed as unsuitable, and Handel's 'My heart ever faithful' put in its place.

I wonder how Nora really felt during the busy summer months before our marriage; probably an increasing irritation that so much had to be done. When Erasmus changed the wedding date to fit in with his work and more important still allow us a longer honeymoon she didn't try to conceal her exasperation in a letter she wrote to him,

'I don't really mind about the wedding and if the notices are ever printed they ought to go out soon. It may annoy some of the people who have been told it is to be on the 4th; but luckily *we* have nothing definitely fixed for the 9th. It will be less convenient for Grandmama and Aunt Ruth as they will have to come again on the 9th but unless they have fixed anything they will not mind. Also I know Aunt Esther and Penny have made special arrangements for the 4th – – Altogether you must expect a certain amount of justifiable cursing if you shift your date, but I darsay it is worthwhile. Can the clergyman marry you on the 9th, and are you sure you can have the church? I really personally do not mind in the least. . . .' Or did she mean 'I really personally do not mind in the least if the wedding never takes place. . . .' The anonymous clergyman she referred to was my first cousin –Ambrose Watson. We were being married in a church, that was bad enough, but having a relation who had taken holy orders –well, less said about that the better.

The social tempo increased as the wedding approached and any attempt at serious studying dwindled to my attending one or two lectures a week. No one minded, it wasn't that sort of a course, and already several students had dropped out – my friend, Roy Lewis, being the first to go.

I stayed a night with Ruth Darwin, Miss Darwin she was to me until that moment over breakfast when she asked me to call her Aunt Ruth. She had a little house on the top of Campden Hill with a Finnish maid whose dipped-in-milk appearance blended in with the brown and white striped curtains, oatmeal carpets and beige walls.

We went with Keynes to the ballet 'Job'. Gwen Raverat had designed the sets. I thought it was marvellous, of course I did, it was all such a treat and I had never set foot in Covent Garden before. Geoffrey liked to be able to see the dancers' feet but from our superb seats in the front row of the dress circle that was not the part of the dancers' anatomy of which we had the best view. We enjoyed a surreptitious snigger over that. I often feel deeply ashamed over our early attitude to Geoffrey. He was such an exceptionally gifted and courageous man. During the First World War he applied his surgical skills under the adverse circumstances of front line warfare with great success. He also invented an operation on the thyroid which revolutionised the medical world. There seemed to be nothing Geoffrey had not read, and everything he read came out of a beautifully bound book, a book as beautiful and well preserved as himself. Once at dinner, he confided in me – it flattered me to think it was a confidence – that at an early age he decided to be the world authority on something artistic. He was always overshadowed by his brilliant brother Maynard and this no doubt gave him the impetus to find a way of excelling himself. Blake offered scope for him to fulfill his ambition. There was no world authority on Blake and Geoffrey with single minded determination went ahead to fill the gap. He made the union sound like a shot-gun wedding rather than a love match but I don't believe it was as cold blooded as that.

The Keynes' had a country house in Suffolk which Nora took me to see on our way to Norfolk. Stephen was detailed to show me yet another Darwin home. I remember his pink, excited face as he threw open door after door displaying yet another lovely room. Margaret's houses were part of herself and Nora, even at her most critical, never questioned her cousin's gift for creating a beautiful home.

I soon came to feel that everything in Margaret's house was too contrived and grew bored with being made to look at this and that, and listen to some anecdote which usually involved a reference to the family tree, about how it had come to be where it was. Margaret's sister, Gwen Raverat, without so much effort and fuss, achieved as good a result – that was my opinion, one which I didn't dare voice.

A visit to Sir Thomas Barlow's sister, Annie, in Manchester, had the added excitement of dinner on the train as it swept through stations and countryside which I had never seen before. I slept in a huge bedroom overlooking the garden where peacocks strutted and emitted agonising shrieks.

This remarkable old lady remained active and extrovert in spite of crippling rheumatoid arthritis. Knotted hands, twisted joints were never allowed to interfere with her good works and while she was dying upstairs in her bedroom a garden party in aid of some charity was taking place on the lawns below.

Another memorable week-end took place at the Kidd's Mill, on the River Test. The lilies of the valley were just out and I could smell their scent when we explored the garden in the evening's half light.

A strange sensation crept over me as we walked along the river bank. I had been here before. Slowly memories of a camping holiday with my brothers came back. In this same river, probably at the exact spot where a notice said 'fishing prohibited', Tam had waded into the water with his trousers off and his shirt tucked into his pants to practise the considerable art of tickling trout. Fish after fish was thrown on the bank where my sister and I had the unpleasant job of banging their heads with a stone while they flapped their tails and gasped for breath. We cooked them on a bonfire high up on the hills overlooking the River Test which the mill straddled and where the talk at dinner was about the iniquities of poachers,

'The gamekeeper does his best, but it's an uphill job to keep them off private property. . . .'

Another health hazard put a temporary spoke in the wheel of the wedding plans. An attack of flu hit me while staying with the Barlows at Hillside in West Runton. A sample of my water was said to contain bacillus coli, quite a serious complaint, which meant the wedding might have to be postponed. In the thirties misdiagnosis was not uncommon. My sister had been misdiagnosed as having Hodgkins disease because of a few swollen glands in her neck. My father's pains in his chest before his fatal coronary were dismissed as indigestion and now for a few days I was thought to be very ill. When the mistake was rectified my mother got it into her head that I was disappointed that everything could now go ahead as planned. A splendid example of projection, perhaps? She quizzed me about my inner fears and back again we went to the problem of birth control. The very words –birth control – produced floods of tears and slamming doors.

Unable to communicate with me, my mother wrote to Erasmus about what she called the sensitive subject of excluding a family for the time being. In her opinion her daughter was suffering from 'nervous exhaustion' and 'nearing the end of her emotional tether', not so much from the psychology course and the wedding plans, but because of 'the corroding dread' of having to practise birth control. Letters went to and fro between my mother and her future son-in-law. They discussed in depth all possible methods, the pros and cons of dutch cap, sheath and the pin. Nora drawn into the tangle of indecision invited me to lunch. When we were alone together she suggested a walk up the herbaceous border where at the end there was a seat conveniently placed for us to sit down on. The scene was set for an intimate talk but Nora was too embarrassed to begin so I took the initiative and plunged in at the deep end with,

'I'm not in the least worried about sex. I know I shall enjoy that,' hoping to put her at her ease, but instead of a smile of approbation her lips went into a straight line. It took her a few minutes to recover, and when we began to talk again the conversation was on the bees and flowers level until quite suddenly, out of the blue, she remarked *en passant*,

'I was dilated before I got married, perhaps it would be a good idea if you were done too.'

What on earth did she mean? Or rather, did she mean what I thought she meant, in which case this was yet another horror to be faced before the wedding night? Why was this trial by fire and water necessary? Why couldn't we just get married without any fuss and spend the night beneath the pine trees embracing between a couple of old blankets instead of all this spine-chilling talk about visiting a gynaecologist in Harley Street whom Nora had visited herself.

'I could make the appointment for you. Her name is Miss Darnley. I am sure you would find her very sympathetic and kind,' Nora said. Trying to be sensible while on the brink of tears I mumbled agreement and then quickly added, 'But not yet,' playing for time.

My mother had the idea that I should talk to a young married friend of Erasmus's who had been a nurse and was therefore a sensible, level-headed person who would also be near enough my own age to broach the difficult subject of birth control. Flora Sinclair, having been primed, duitfully invitied me to tea in her flat, not far from Great James Street where I was going to live. She had made a great effort on my behalf, scones, jam, cake and a cat in a basket with a lot of lovely kittens as a conversation piece before the really important topic was broached. I ate the scones, drank the tea and listened to the advantages of a dutch cap over a pin.

'Much safer and more hygienic,' she explained; 'as for that ghastly french letter – my husband refuses to use it. He says it's like eating a toffee with the wrapping paper left on.'

Dreading more intimate revelations I switched my attention to the cat purring contentedly in the basket. Kittens kneaded her belly with their paws while they sucked away at her teats. I could identify with the cat, but kind Flora with her

tea and good advice left me in no better state that I had
been before.

Someone had to take action, and someone did. Nora made
an appointment for me to go to Miss Darnley's chamber of
horrors a couple of days before the wedding. That was far
enough away at the moment for me to pretend it would never
happen. Much nicer to think about our honeymoon plans
instead.

My mother wanted us to go where there would be amusement and stimulation. Nora advised the opposite. We would
be exhausted, she said, but did not disclose from what. She
just insisted on our need to rest. In spite of my mother's retort
that what was right for a Barlow was not necessarily right for a
Black, Nora found a small hotel on a muddy little bay in West
Sussex. She booked a room for us overlooking the water
where we agreed to do as we were told and rest for a few days
before leaving for France on the Channel ferry. We were
allowed to borrow the car for our time in England but not for
driving around on the Continent which was what Erasmus
wanted, of course.

Since the wedding was to be rather small with numbers
limited to relations and close friends Nora agreed to have a
garden party at Boswells for those who would have felt left out
if they had not been invited to some sort of function connected with our marriage. Aunt Helen's wish for a tenants' tea fitted in neatly with this arrangement. The marquee could be
used for both occasions – that satisfied what the family called
her love of mosaics.

Dear Aunt Helen, I marvelled at the easy way she dealt with
those tenants during the sticky tea in the huge marquee on
that hot July day. Although Aunt Helen addressed them simply as Sharp, Bean, Edith, etc, without any handles attached to
their names, she was always at one with them, laughing and
talking and tucking into the buns with the same enthusiasm as
they did. She had master-planned this show. Nora, lacking
her sister-in-law's indiscriminate love of the human race, was
pleased to let her get on with it and stayed very much in
the background.

I did my smiling best behind the tea urn and chatted
whenever there was any sign of response, but none of the
tenants seemed in the least interested in Erasmus or me. They

said 'Pleased to meet you' when introduced and then turned their backs and made a bee-line for someone they knew. I began to feel I had done something wrong and blamed my clothes for their off-hand behaviour. Perhaps I should have dressed up for the occasion. I noticed Aunt Helen was wearing her Sunday best – a floral print, pulled in at the waist with an expensive belt and an impressive straw hat. *And* gloves, *and* thick lisle stockings *and* sensible shoes with heels that didn't sink into the grass. I wanted to go home and exchange my village dressmaker cotton frock and strapless sandals for the clothes I was going to wear at the garden party the next day. That very special long sleeved silk dress – yes, I had acquired it at last thanks to Nora – the hat with a veil, and all the matching accessories would have impressed them, but it was too late now.

After tea the indefatigable Aunt Helen introduced a little light entertainment into the afternoon, a variation of 'What the Butler Saw', a preview of my trousseau. It was her overwhelming desire for involvement that lay behind this appalling idea and only from fear of offending her had I agreed to having my underwear put on show, draped over he drawing-room furniture. All that beautiful hand-stitched satin, silk and crepe-de-chine intended for only Erasmus to see was gawped at and muttered over by the tenants as I kept watch like a sentry at a lying-in-state.

And that was not all. There was still the agony on the verandah where a selection of our wedding presents were displayed. Every shape and size Pyrex dish was there. Why, how, could two people have so many possessions? I felt bloated by the too muchness of it all. Willingly would I have presented a Pyrex dish to each of those tenants who queued up to shake hands with me. The party was over but Aunt Helen still had enough energy to walk down the drive with the gardener's wife listening to a tale of woe about a dying relative, or was it a sick child? Erasmus, Nora and I, sagging at the knees, crept back into the drawing-room and collapsed into chairs.

'Thank goodness they've all gone,' Nora said, 'I hope it wasn't too much of an ordeal for you both.'

'Aunt Helen enjoyed it,' I replied, but Erasmus, less diplomatic and more honest than I, added,

'If only she'd pep up the alcoholic content of the fruit cup.'

The next day I was back again at Boswells for a garden party which owing to Alan's recent knighthood turned out to be an occasion to congratulate him as well as to pay respects to the future newly-weds. Nora had taken the news of his 'K' with the minimum of delight. It was his due, an inevitable consequence of his work in the Civil Service. Alan had shown no reaction at all. Nothing would change the pattern of his life – weekdays in London working at the Treasury and playing bridge at the Savile club late into the night. For the weekends at Boswells he always wore his oldest, shabbiest clothes and divided his time between cutting down trees and tending the compost heap. This Saturday was different. He looked martyred when he appeared in his dark London suit, well fortified with alcohol, to receive the guests. We stood in line on the verandah and many of the guests were so eager to congratulate Alan on his knighthood that they by-passed us. An extraordinary hotpotch of people were there – a German delegation arrived, heaven knows why they were asked. Sir John Reith, with his bushy eyebrows, a perfect subject for the cartoonists stood head and shoulders above the crowd. A group from Chesham Bois greeted me with great warmth and friendliness but showed no inclination to be introduced to anyone else. A few of the guests stayed on for a dinner that night. I sat next to Edward Bridges who talked at me with great profoundness about marriage. The trouble is I can not remember a word or what he said although the sensation of profundity remains to this day.

Looking back on the week of the wedding the juxtaposition of events amazes me. We were to be married on Saturday and on Thursday Erasmus drove me up to London and left me on the pavement outside a door in Harley Street. He wished me 'good luck', but I needed more than that to drag myself up the steps and press the bell above the brass plate which said 'Patients'.

I felt sick, of course, and wondered if I was going to faint when the brusque receptionist in a crackling white coat escorted me like a prisoner into the waiting room where minutes seemed like hours before my name was called. Jelly legs almost refused to carry me across the floor to the consulting room with the terrible smell of lurking anaesthetic and Miss Darnley's no panic smile as she shook hands with me. She tried to be kind and deal with me gently but I shrank from everything she asked me to do. Remove knickers, lie down on couch, open legs wide, wide, wide apart. She explained about dilation and then like a conjuror produced from nowhere a glass phallus. First a small one, then a bigger one and then, yes, she showed me the blood after the first agonising penetration had been made. I was crimson in the face and fighting back my tears by the time she had finished what she referred to as 'that little job'. A short pause as though it was half time in a strenuous hockey match, only no oranges, just a sip of water to keep up my strength while a Dutch cap was fitted. Yes, she found the right size but now I had to learn to put it in and take it out. Easier said than done. I squatted down on the floor and tried to do exactly as she said, while the wretched cap first refused to slip into place and then disappeared when I wanted to bring it out.

'All you have to do it insert a finger, find the rim and give a gentle tug,' she said, her voice straining to be patient. I tried again and felt a fleeting triumph when – squelch – out it came, shooting across the floor and landing at Miss Darnleys's feet. Back again on the couch while she put it in herself with a lot of encouraging talk about safety and how is could stay there a whole week, but by now I was crying helplessly and she with a worried face watched me put on my knickers and said,

'My dear, are you sure you are really ready for marriage?'

'Too late to call it off now,' I said, 'the wedding is the day after tomorrow.'

Besides, I was to meet my future father-in-law at the Athenaeum annexe for lunch and I was already running out of time. I certainly could not envisage myself going up to him and saying,

'Sorry the wedding is not going to take place after all, the gynaecologist has prepared me for the nuptial bed but she says I'm not ready for marriage yet.'

I took a taxi down to the Mall and arrived at the annexe of this stronghold for men to find Alan already waiting for me with a glass in his hand. I refused a drink and sped to the cloakroom where swansdown puffs in bowls of powder, hot water and piles of clean towels helped me to do something about my bedraggled appearance. I felt and looked as though I had been pulled through a prickly hedge forwards and backwards.

We sat at a small table near the window. Conversation was never Alan's strong point. If we could had had *The Times* crossword to do that would have saved the effort of thinking of something to say. I praised the scorched melba toast and he praised the mauve pâté. Our talk never included any reference to his son marrying me. We might have been two strangers meeting for the first time. Only after the coffee had been served did I discover the purpose for this lunch. He wanted to buy me a wedding present, one strictly for myself, he said. We walked up the Burlington arcade to a shop where the assistant had obviously been forewarned of our visit. The glass counter was covered with a velvet cloth and from a case of jewels I was told to select what I liked. No price tags to guide me to the cheapest, just a bewildering glitter of gold, silver and expensive stones. His generosity failed to spark off any emotion in me because he seemed so unemotional himself. I remembered the intense experience of choosing my engagement ring; compared with that this seemed to be part of the cold-blooded ritual which had begun that morning in Harley Street. It took years for me to recognise and appreciate Alan's latent heat. He stood by me now, waiting for me to make up my mind, saying nothing, giving the occasional sniff and showing just the faintest reaction when I chose a seed pearl necklace with matching earrings.

I returned home with two trophies from my day's outing in town – a leather jewel case with the pearls inside and a cardboard package containing the birth control. That night my sister came into the bathroom while I was lying in the bath.

'You're no longer a virgin,' she said. After all the trauma I had been through to achieve that state I didn't know whether to laugh or cry. I gave what I hoped was an enigmatic smile and thought 'Oh dear.'

The next day I was convinced I could feel the new contraption inside me and was grateful to the spinster aunts whose arrival with their demands for comfort, warmth and food provided a distraction from morbid thoughts. Everyone had the superficial calm of the first night of a well-rehearsed play but I had to escape from the smiles, the questioning looks, the endless talk about the weather and what to do if it rained and could the reception be held in doors.

With the excuse that I must finish my packing I went upstairs to my bedroom where my luggage, locked and labelled, seemed to be waiting for the next day as impatiently as myself. Thanks to Lady Darwin's substantial wedding present cheque our honeymoon had been extended to include a short stay in Paris which meant that clothes suitable for town and country had to be squeezed into a suitcase. Strange as it may seem nowadays I was also taking with me a hat box, in which tucked away beside my hats, logically enough perhaps, lay my dutch cap container with its partners in crime, the ghoulish instructions and foul smelling jelly.

I went to bed early and lay awake listening to the rain, worrying that I was worrying, and that if I didn't sleep I would never be the radiant bride tomorrow. And then suddenly it was tomorrow. The rain had stopped and although the sky was grey there was a lightening in the East and just enough hint of sunshine behind the clouds to hope the day would be fine.

I was given breakfast in bed, scrambled eggs and bacon and told to eat it ALL up – like the proverbial calf I had to be fattened for the sacrifice. Every minute was scheduled – a visit to the hairdresser where I suffered and squirmed under the dryer, insisting my hair was dry when it was still sopping wet, was followed by vacating my bedroom and spreading out my wedding clothes on my parents' bed. I moved like an automaton from job to job; if I could not make enough effort with the aunts that would be forgiven because for once none of my mother's strict rules of social conduct applied to me today. I had bridal immunity.

Lunch over, I went upstairs to change, putting on my white satin underwear and feeling rather draughty in french knickers with no elastic round my thighs. My mother hovered over me. She had had her final say the week before,

'I am thankful you will never stick anything out if you're miserable. I should hate to think of you putting up with an unhappy marriage just for respectability's sake.'

No pessimistic talk now. This was a 'happy ever after' script. The production went ahead smoothly with unexpected touch of comedy injected by Tam. When the banns, which had been left behind at the house, were needed at the church, someone called to Tam, 'Go and get the banns', and he, not realising it was an official document that had to be fetched, went to the station to meet a couple called Mr and Mrs Bans off the train.

When the bridal car arrived on cue with white ribbons streaming, my father appeared in his frock coat which he was determined to wear, because it was hanging in his cupboard, even if none of the other guests would be in morning dress. My voluminous tulle veil, held in place by the dark red roses from Boswells, had to be manipulated into the car before we sat down. He took my hand. He was a sentimental man who would cry over his own stories and this was a moment when I should have said some loving word, but dreading an emotional scene and feeling as always the oppression of his total love for me, I withdrew my hand from his warm clasp and shrank as far as my veil allowed to the other side of the car. Stony hearted, I regret it now.

The bridesmaids were waiting at the lych-gate for us to arrive and their smiles widened at the bride's expletive when a thorn caught her billowing veil. Inside, the church was a mass of flowers and faces with Erasmus standing beside his best man, John Kidd. My cousin Ambrose transformed into a priest by his dog collar and surplice explained to the congregation why they were there and then set about the serious business of joining us together in holy matrimony. When I took Erasmus's hand it was trembling. I tightened my grasp and over-eager came in too early with my wedding vows. It took three attempts for me to say 'I will' in the right place.

Kneeling at the alter a peace descended on me. All the fripperies of the wedding lost their importance and I thought: This is serious, now I must pray. I prayed to be a good wife – whether that prayer has been answered is doubtful, perhaps, but all I can say is that without that prayer I might have been a worse wife.

The signing of the register with Elisabeth Raverat singing 'My heart ever faithful', her beautiful voice barely audible through the babble as I wrote my name, Brigit Black, for the last time. Down the aisle on my husband's arm with my veil swept back; bells ringing as we stood outside the church to be photographed. Into the car and back to the house. Everything moving very fast like an old-fashioned film so that no sooner had we shaken all the hands than we were standing on the verandah listening to Dr. Addison now a Labour peer, make his speech which everyone noisily applauded more for its brevity than its content. Champagne with the cutting of the cake, Erasmus and I held the knife together and laughed when the icing resisted the sharp blade. Guests sat at small tables under the trees while daily women smartened up with clean white aprons waited on them, running to and fro from the house with food that a local woman had prepared.

Time to change. It was the bridesmaids' job to help the bride but they were outside enjoying themselves too much to worry about this final ritual. My mother, slightly flushed from social effort and repressed emotion, sat on the bed watching me exchange my bridal attire for a pink shantung two-piece. We did not speak. Silence transcended any words that we might have said. It had been a good party, I told myself, refusing to think this was one of the most important days of my life. I powdered my nose, arranged my curls under my hat; what mattered now was the present. My mother put a pound note into my bag but I took it out and gave it back to her.

'I'm no longer your financial burden,' I said, and accepted a florin instead. We laughed at the size of my dowry and then while the laughter was still there we embraced without shedding a tear.

Outside a crowd gathered round the car and I am left with a collage of impressions. A chicken on top of the roof of the car – it had escaped from its run and Tam put it there. Horace wiping his eye – was he crying? Nora's hat, a wonderful 'that will do' concoction of black lace and battered straw. I don't remember kissing my father goodbye but I remember my father-in-law's kiss on the lips, warm and dry. My mother's anxious face – were we going to manage all right? No, we weren't. We had only got half way up the hill when we had to turn back. The hat box had been left behind. Freud had struck again.

When we arrived at the hotel I got out of the car with a shower of confetti landing at my feet. 'Much happiness,' the manageress said, and took us up to our bedroom overlooking the creek. A large double bed with a pink shiny eiderdown seemed to be the only piece of furniture; the chest of drawers and wardrobe, table and chairs dwindled in significance beside it. We put our luggage on top of the pink satin, took turns to go to the bathroom and then went down for dinner – salmon and champagne. A walk along a muddy footpath, a sunset to admire whiled away the time till we could say 'Let's go to bed.'

We explored the South Coast in the car, which after a few days of energetic 'rest' we left at Dover for Bean to collect. We slept in the sun on the channel ferry and lay awake in each other's arms as the *wagon-lits* argued with the railway track on our night journey through France. We found a small pension on the foothills of the Alps. The grass was packed with flowers and we hunted for their names in a flora Erasmus had remembered to pack. We bought ourselves penny whistles and transposed folk songs into duets from a second-hand music book found in the market

We bathed naked in streams and walked in the mountains. We spent a night in a wooden hut high up above the snow line. There was a punch-up between two male climbers over a young man whom we noticed had been wearing lipstick at supper. We lost our way going back, scrambled for hours along slippery scree, got hopelessly sunburnt, found it agony to sleep apart and agony when our burning limbs made contact. We travelled further up the valley by jumping on the back of a slow moving lorry without the driver being aware that we were there. We ate our way through enormous meals, drank wine, and ran out of money on our way home after a few clammy hours in Paris.

7

We returned to England and went straight to Boswells without first visiting the flat. There was still nearly a week left of Erasmus's holiday and I had no desire to be in London any earlier than need be. We found Nora in the garden with Joan. They were topping and tailing gooseberries, sitting on a seat, in the shade of a tree. Nora looked up and her initial pleasure at seeing us gave way to her anxious expression as though there was a huge question mark over her head. She wouldn't ask the question she wanted to ask because that would have been indelicate. A pity, because in spite of our inexperience, my answer would have been reassuring.

I settled down very easily into the life at Boswells after our honeymoon. We slept in the room Erasmus had shared with Andrew which was in the green lino zone, beyond the swing doors, overlooking the yard, and opposite the bedroom of Susan, their old nanny. She had stayed on with the family since the Chesham Bois days to rule the brooms, brushes and dusters in the housemaid cupboard with the same zeal as she had ruled the children in the nursery before they all grew up. She belonged to a strict religious sect and accepted the Devil but not a God of love. She talked to herself and occasionally broke into a mournful dirge only recognisable as a hymn if one already knew the words. At first I thought this hymn singing expressed her religious fervour but I soon discovered it was her only means of showing her disapproval of the pagan household in which she lived.

A lot of hymn singing went on when Theo Winter, Erasmus's cousin, a Barlow, came to stay, with her husband, Carl. Theo, in the early days of her pregnancy, had been ordered by her doctor to rest to avoid a threatened miscarriage. She lay on the sofa in the school-room and was easily accessible for conversation, or rather, gossip. Occasionally the juicier bits must have been overheard by Susan because every now and then her beholding the wondrous cross outside the door grew so loud that we could hardly hear was each other was saying.

That year there was a glut of wild strawberries. We went to the Round Hill and filled huge bowls with them to be eaten in vast quantities covered in thick cream from the farm dairy for dinner that night. We also picked mushrooms in the fields; Carl had theories about how mushrooms should be cooked – with wine, garlic and cream, sophisticated things like that, which were far beyond anything I had learned at the Chelsea Polytechnic.

When the day came for us to take up residence in the flat Nora loaded us with farm produce, bunches of dahlias and a basket of the mushrooms which, inspired by Carl, I was longing to cook. We borrowed the car in order to take our wedding presents to London. The Pyrex dishes were piled on to the back seat. We had decided to leave the rest of our presents in tea chests in the loft to be unpacked at a later date –a much later date, did we but know.

As we drove to London through the pouring rain I tried to be cheerful but the mournful whine of the windscreen wipers echoed my true mood. The sight of a crumpled car and broken glass all over the road increased my dejection.

When we arrived at 26 Great James Street I had no wish to be carried over the threshold, even if Erasmus had suggested it. Immediately we opened the front door the caretaker emerged down the dark passage through the stench of cat, and stood with one hand on the banister watching us carry our luggage up to the flat. The Boswells' loot left no room for the wedding present boxes, which had to be left outside on the landing.

Erasmus looked at his watch and I looked out at the grey London day. Not a tree in sight, just roof tops and chimneys; it could be any season of the year.

'I'll have to go,' he said, 'There's a lecture at ten o'clock and I'll be late back because of out-patients in the afternoon.'

He kissed me goodbye, a distracted kiss as though he was already half way to the hospital. When the door closed I quelled impending panic by vigorous action. I bustled around the flat, tearing down the striped bedspreads that covered the wall, and removing cushions that clashed with the hearth rug. This was my home, I told myself over and over again, hoping that auto-suggestion would convice me that it was true. I arranged the dahlias in our new Wedgwood vase, and tried to find space in the cramped kitchen for the vegetables Nora had given us. The smell of onions clashed with the scented soap in the bath but I knew I must adapt to the washing conditions; it was like camping without the fresh air. A ventilator tried to conform with the LCC regulations, by blowing a draught through the lavatory over the partition and into the kitchen.

While I was unpacking the boxes on the landing, Martin Pollock emerged from the flat below. He took one cynical glance at the bourgeois sight of the young bride surrounded by her wedding presents and quickly withdrew. A pity, I would have enjoyed a chat, not that Martin was capable of chatting, small talk was an anathema to him, but his disapproval at my conversation would be preferable to this long drawn out morning on my own. A ring at the door bell, hurrah! Something had happened at last. ı rushed to the window and leaned out to see who was there. It was my father. Dressed for London, he was wearing his seeing-an-editor suit and a bowler hat.

'Oh, it's you,' I said, a churlish response to the delight registered on his upturned face.

With the help of his walking stick he puffed his way up the four flights of stairs and sank down into a chair. Having regained his breath he helped me stow away the Pyrex dishes and when that was done suggested we should lunch together in a nearby pub. As I waded through the *specialité* de la maison, steak and kidney pudding, my father kept asking me, phrasing the question differently each time, whether I was alright. He could make me a small allowance for clothes, he said, but I refused this generous offer which I knew he could ill afford.

'We are determined to live within our income,' I said – a tactless remark, since that was something my father had never been able to do.

'We've budgeted for absolutely everything. Thanks to that wonderful trousseau there's no need to buy clothes and my food will be covered by the charwoman's wage. You see, I'll be doing the cleaning myself from now on.'

Unfortunately, the charwoman was the last to know of this arrangement. We found her beavering away in the flat when

we got back after lunch. Alarmed by the effect she would have
on my budget, I ploughed straight in and gave her the sack
there and then. I couldn't understand why she had turned up
for work. Surely she understood that with me in the flat her
services would no longer be required? After a few mild words
of protest she collected her things and made a dignified exit.
My father was appalled by what he called my 'brutal
behaviour.' 'She went quite pink,' he said. He had gone quite
pink himself.

Into a tin labelled 'binge money' I put the spare cash left
over from the house-keeping allowance which Erasmus gave
me each week after going to the bank. I kept a very careful
watch on what we spent and accounted for every item down to
the last halfpenny. We always went away each week-end, either
to my parents or to Boswells and the amount we saved on food
by these visits helped to fill up the 'binge money' tin very quickly. We were soon flush enough to throw a party but in fact
the party threw us. We had never entertained together before
marriage, a grievous error, and from the moment the guests
arrived we paid heavily for our lack of experience. They were a
mixed bag of friends and relations who refused to mix. Nora
and her sister Ruth sat together on the sofa offering to help but
the party was beyond help; perfectly reasonable people who
could sustain an interesting conversation in other circumstances turned into stuffed dummies incapable of saying anything
beyond 'yes, please,' or 'no thank you,' to the cheap sherry
and limp biscuits which we offered them. When they had all
gone very promptly, if not before the deadline of eight
o'clock, we cleared up the mess and then crawled into bed. We
wanted to spare each other's feelings. In the dark we cuddled
up close together and inveighed against our guests, blaming
them rather than ourselves for the party's lack of success.

We tried again. No more bulk entertaining this time, just a
cosy supper for two friends, a married couple, newly-weds like
ourselves, Angela and Ben Burns. I ironed the best organdie
peach-coloured mats and laid the places with everything that
might be required north, south, west and east of the vase of
flowers in the centre of the table. We lacked a parlour maid
standing with her back to the sideboard and a gong booming us
into dinner; nevertheless it was as near as I could get to imitating
Saturday night at Boswells until my table's symmetry was

spoiled by one guest arriving instead of two. Ben had come alone.

No lack of conversation on this social occasion. Chamberlain's visit to Germany and Hitler's demands in Czechoslovakia were discussed, only it ws scarcely a discussion, because Ben and Erasmus held identical views based, I felt sure, on what they had read in the *Daily Worker* that morning. As they became more and more heated about the iniquitous attitude of the government they leaned on the table with their elbows, crumpling my exquisite mats, lashing out with a hand and spilling wine, and forgetting to use that ultimate refinement, the butter knife. Feeling I knew in advance what was going to be said I was surprised when Ben announced,

'I've sent Angela to the country, what are you going to do with Biddy?'

I realised he really believed there was going to be a war. The next day the political situation worsened after another visit by Chamberlain to the Munich conference. Sandbags appeared in the streets and a desultory digging with a lot of leaning on spades began in the parks. When Erasmus volunteered to stay in the hospital full-time to deal with air-raid casualties I agreed to being another wife sent to the country.

At Boswells Nora wasn't there to give her usual welcome. She had embarked on a Red Cross course which meant attending lectures all day in Wendover. Andrew, Hilda and I lolled around in front of the fire, felt guilty, and decided to follow Nora's good example by doing something useful. We walked down to Witchel Meadow and joined the small crowd watching an ARP demonstration. A nervous young man wearing a tin hat to add a touch of authenticity to the occasion poured a small mixture of magnesium and iron filings on to a plate and shaped it into a neat little heap as though giving a cookery demonstration.

'This is an incendiary bomb,' he announced, and put a match to it. He stood back expecting a huge bang, but there were only a few half-hearted splutters, the sort of thing a damp squib might give. Everyone smiled.

'And this is how you put it out,' he said, taking a handful of sand from a bucket, ignoring the fact that a gentle breeze had already done the job for him. The crowd applauded and dispersed, quite pleased with the afternoon's entertainment.

In the evening we listened to the nine o'clock news, worried over what we heard and then forgot out worries in a game of racing demon played on the schoolroom table. When Chamberlain went on his third mission to Germany to meet Hitler in Munich we resigned ourselves to war being inevitable. It was only a matter of time before the bombs began to fall, not nice, gentle, spluttering benign bombs like we had seen at the demonstration, but megatons of death dropping out of the sky. So. . . we went to the cinema in Aylesbury and tried to escape from the tension by watching a film called '*A Yank at Oxford*'. Two hours later we emerged from the celluloid world into an equally unreal one with the newspaper boys shouting the success of Chamberlain's mission. Peace in our time. Or as it turned out – peace to give us time to prepare for war.

Alan decided to celebrate Chamberlain's victorious return from Munich by giving a large dinner party at the Athenaeum annexe, to which we were invited. Erasmus, disgusted with the policy of appeasement, had already had some stormy arguments with his father and I was surprised he could sink his principles so easily for the sake of an evening out.

'If you quarrel with your father tonight,' I warned him, 'I shall get down from my chair, crawl under the table and not come out until you've stopped.'

Erasmus laughed at the thought of such a comical scene taking place in the sedate Athenaeum. 'I shan't say anything,' he promised. He kept his word but managed a protest nevertheless. When Alan toasted Neville Chamberlain as the great hero who had saved the country from war, Erasmus, alone, failed to raise his glass.

I returned to University College as a married student, quite a rarity in those days, and encountered unforeseen problems. I had never been much good at taking notes from a droning professor in a stuffy lecture theatre but now, distracted by what I had left cooking in preparation for supper, concentration became almost impossible. No pearls of wisdom from Freud, Jung or Adler could compete with what mattered now – had I left the gas on too high or should I have turned it down to regulo two?

Without really being aware of Nora's influence I ran the flat very much in accordance with her standards. Meals appeared on time, the table properly laid, the food not slopped out of a saucepan on to plates but arranged appetisingly with sprigs of parsley and served from one of the many Pyrex dishes. I wore a colourful printed overall at breakfast and changed from student clothes into something more glamorous at night. It was hard work keeping up with the Boswell Joneses in conditions more suitable for a bohemian style of life.

The plumbing remained the worst feature of the flat. I hated pushing up the kitchen table and finding mutton fat in the bath and cleaning my teeth into a sink where cooking remains congested the plug hole. As for following Miss Darnley's instructions, that required a contortionist's skill, and I had to crouch down between the gas stove and the refrigerator while balancing the contraceptive device on top of a saucepan lid. However, the birth control, in spite of its unaesthetic aggravations, worked, and Tam's joke about a dutch cap club for all the babies conceived with this method in use, seemed unjustified until the eclipe of the moon.

Not such a *non sequitur* as it seems to be. One thing led to another; Martin Pollock set the chain of events in motion by dragging us out of our first sleep when he shouted from the flat below. We thought it was a fire, or the beginning of the war, until we looked out of the window and saw a dark shadow, like the hand of God, covering the face of the moon. It was a warm, still night and the rumbling trams in Theobald's Road sounded louder than usual. Filled with a strange excitement at the primeval sight, we stood close together, watching the eclipse of the moon until the urge to get back into bed became too great; although we weren't ready for sleep, neither were we fully awake.

I was reading Freud's *Totem and Taboo* when Erasmus telephoned from the hospital that my pregnancy test was positive. He informed his friends straight away, sending telegrams if necessary, and his enthusiasm buoyed me up through the shock of this sudden assault on my body by symptoms which I could no longer dismiss as psychological.

Martin Pollock was delighted with the news. He maintained he had played an important part in the conception of Jeremy. We called him Jeremy from the very start, not after someone in the family, but after the koala bear which Erasmus gave me when we got engaged. Perhaps if we had plucked a name from the family tree – Charles, Robert, Josiah – that might have sweetened Nora's expression when we talked about her future grandchild whom she seemed to view as a calamity rather than a blessing.

Determined to be realistic she sat in front of the school-room two bar electric fire and gave a chilling account of what motherhood involved while I huddled close to the radiator trying to ward off the fear induced by what she said. Bad nights. No one had ever mentioned that to me before. Was I really expected to lose sleep? Of course. Babies cried at night and if Erasmus was kept awake his work would inevitably suffer and he would fail his exams. She mentioned a monthly nurse, an added horror, at her expense of course, who would take charge of the baby when I came out of hospital, the assumption being that I would go straight to Boswells. Further more, when I had given birth Erasmus would be in need of a holiday, and she strongly advised he should go away with some of his university friends for a week's mountain climbing in Scotland. It sounded like a cleansing process, the male equivalent of the churching of women.

The idea of Erasmus going away and not being there to help me with the baby was the last straw. She must have realised that in her desire to prepare me for the future she had gone too far. As I left the room with a tremulous 'good night' she caught hold of my hand and in a gentle tone of cautious optimism said,

'I am sure it will be a very nice Jeremy.'

My mother took a very different view from Nora's. She was ecstatic at the news. From now on Erasmus could do no wrong. He was the perfect son-in-law.

'You've married your father,' she said, and added, 'only Erasmus is a better provider.' She rhapsodised over the joys of motherhood, the new dimension that a baby would bring to our lives, the deep satisfaction of breast feeding. All her memories of giving birth were happy ones. She had never experienced the trauma that Nora had suffered with the birth of Joan. I was grateful to my mother for her rose tinted spectacles which saw babies as undiluted pleasure until she began eulogising over the smell of nappies airing in front of the fire; only she used a more romantic word than 'smell'. I knew that was what she meant because everything smelled now. I tried to combat the smells in the flat by buying joss sticks and burning them at strategic spots, but soon their pungent synthetic sweetness became worse than the more basic smells of lavatory, cooking and sink.

I was being an absolute pest. I knew it and couldn't stop, which made sympathy coming from a most unexpected quarter greatly valued. After dinner one evening at Boswells, Alan in his velvet smoking jacket and skew-wiff bow tie sat beside me in front of the log fire; he took out a cigar and was about to light up when he hesitated, and asked whether I would mind the smell of smoke.

'Nora in your condition could never bear the smell of smoke,' he said. This small incident cheered me up, not only because of the oblique reference to his future grandchild, whose existence he hadn't recognised before, but because it showed that Nora had fallen prey to one of my symptoms. Perhaps she wasn't quite so tough after all.

I began to feel less sick but remained very static, fearful that any exertion might make the baby drop out. I watched the family build a bonfire with tremendous energy and did not lift a hand to help until Nora told me to move about more.

My first visit to the ante-natal clinic in University College Hospital reassured me everything was perfectly normal. Miss Dodd, the obstetrician, had a severe haircut and soft brown eyes. She prodded my tummy very gently, answered all my questions, while a queue of mothers and wailing babies waited outside. Having discussed my fears she decided that a public ward was not the place for me. I should go, when the time comes, to a nursing home with a room of my own and enough fresh air from a window to open and close as I liked. She mentioned several nursing homes where she could come from UCH to deliver me, and although she warned me that the labour would be 'no picnic' I felt encouraged by my visit.

At the reception desk where I made my next appointment I received a pink card with the baby's expected date of arrival on it which looked like a timetable. The train due on July 30th would be delivered by Miss Dodds, only Miss Dodds thought it would probably be later than that. She pinned her faith to scientific calculation rather than my ramblings about the eclipse of the moon.

When the term began in January I announced that I was

giving up my psychology course. This important piece of decision-making came not with a blinding light on the way to University College but in a flash of realism while standing by the kitchen sink. There could be no compromise with Erasmus's work. His training as a doctor had top priority in our life. Looking after a baby was a full time job, therefore something had to go. Gazing out on the roof tops with chimneys pouring smoke into the bleak January sky I said goodbye to my friends, Freud, Adler and Jung and any hope I had of a career of my own.

I also made another decision, one that was less welcomed by Nora. We must move. At last, the perfect excuse for getting out of the flat I had never liked.

'Impossible to manage a baby in a flat up four flights of stairs,' I said.

'But a move would be such a disruption,' she replied. I knew she was thinking about Erasmus's work and that other mothers managed in a flat, so why couldn't I?

'What about the fresh air?' I asked, visualising myself proudly pushing a pram with a frilly canopy.

'Pram pushing is a waste of time. Something to keep the nanny happy rather than do the baby any good. A carry-cot beside an open window is as good, or even a wooden drawer would do,' she said.

'But the smuts from the chimneys blow into the room if the windows are open, I can't even dry our washing there,' I argued. Neither of us mentioned a nappy service, that would have been a far too decadent solution – better move into a basement flat in a cheaper area north of the park than sink to that.

I trudged in and out of dilapidated houses reeking of dry rot, and soon became painfully aware of the price that would have to be paid for a patch of balding lawn and access to the dog's lavatory with the romantic name of Primrose Hill.

By the end of January I was no nearer to finding a suitable alternative to our flat and was beginning to think that we should make do with what we had got when I awoke one morning feeling rebellious; without telling Erasmus I took a bus to Hampstead in order to explore the possibilities there. Opposite the underground was a house agent, Potters. Guilty at being so far afield, I hesitated. Erasmus would not be able to walk to work from here and that essential clause of the plan had been inserted by Nora. What was wrong with public transport, I thought, and pushed through the swing doors. A bespectacled man rose from behind a desk and offered me a seat in a leather chair. He seemed to have all the time in the world and his sympathetic manner, more suitable for a psychiatrist than someone selling a house, encouraged me to talk, so that I had not only told him about our requirements but also mentioned our expected baby and Nora's views on how we could manage in our flat. 'My mother-in-law says . . .' and 'My mother-in-law thinks . . .' produced a sigh which I took to mean sympathy for me. Quite likely he was beginning to feel sorry for my mother-in-law.

After delving into a filing cabinet he turned to me with an apologetic smile and said,

'Only one possibility, I'm afraid; a cottage in Willow Road. It's a workman's cottage that has been renovated. The rent is a little bit more than you want to pay but maybe the difference could be found?'

'We have some money in our deposit account,' I assured him, sounding quite knowledgeable about our finances even if I didn't really know what a deposit account was.

I walked down Well Walk savouring the address: 38 Willow Road, 38 Willow Road; I said it over and over again to myself until I turned the corner and actually saw the row of cottages. The rush of emotion was so overpowering that I feared it might harm the baby. Willow trees, gold tipped, tossed in the wind; bow windows on the ground floor looked out on front gardens; that 'To Let' sign was the answer to my unspoken prayers.

It was love at first sight, an all embracing love which I find easier to feel for a house than a human being. Nothing could deter me now. I could accept that house without bothering to go inside and discover the warts. But there weren't any warts; it even had a bathroom which in present day jargon would be described as 'en suite with the master bedroom', the only bedroom, in fact, which had two windows overlooking the garden, a muddy strip which was already full of flowers in my imagination.

The rounded, early Victorian windows, which I admired from the outside belonged to the sitting room that led into a

smallish room ideal for Erasmus's study . . . or . . . no . . . yes
. . . the baby's nursery. A basement dining room had a trickle
of daylight and a view of a privet hedge if I stood on tip toe and
craned my neck. The kitchen at the back was the greatest luxury of all. It wasn't doubling up for any other purpose, it was
just a simple, straightforward kitchen with a door opening
into a very small yard where washing could hang on a line
without any fears of smuts.

We moved up to Hampstead in March, the same month
Hitler's troops invaded Czechoslovakia. This shattering event
that changed the map of Europe took second place to the
frenetic nest-building that now began. In the excitement of
acquiring my new home I spared little thought for those
unfortunate Czechs who had lost theirs. Erasmus could now
be congratulated on his vilification of Chamberlain's appeasement policy. He said a lot of 'there you are', 'what did I say'
and 'I told you so', perhaps hoping for an intelligent reply but
I'm afraid that it is not what he got. My head was full of yellow
piping, did it really go with the new rust hessian chair covers
and were the striped, yes the Darwin striped yellow curtains in
the sitting room a little too bright and might not a shade paler
have been better?

We were setting up house properly this time with me very
much in charge, now knowing what I liked and disliked. And
there was a solid lump of money in the bank, not liquid
money that would join the cash flow and float away into an
overdraft, but real money, thanks to the left-wing tenants who
took over the lease of the flat and could afford to pay for the
carpets, the curtains and all the furniture I didn't want.

Nora agreed our cottage was delightful and having
wheedled out of me the cost of the move and made reassuring
noises about 'money was always there' if we got into difficulties. She went into each room saying exactly what she
thought – basement too dark, stairs too steep but at the yellow
striped curtains she gave a nod of approval and said, 'That's
nice,' an understatement, I felt. For me they provided instant
sunshine every time I came into the room. When we went up
to our bedroom she looked at the glazed chintz curtains with a
more critical eye.

'We had curtains rather like these in The Orchard nursery,'
she said, 'only they were lined with similar chintz of a much

smaller pattern.' She paused, fingering the material, and then went on to suggest that mine would hang better if they too were lined.

Such widly extravagant ideas from my prudent mother-in-law! Before she started to yank down the curtains and write out a cheque I told her firmly they would do perfectly well as they were. Cheapest of cheap cambric, perhaps one day, yes, but as for buying more glazed chintz for lining . . . No.

With the warmer weather we started work on the garden which slanted up to a gate that squeaked – a tuneful squeak when it heralded Erasmus's homecoming. We flattened the ground into two terraces and separated them by building a wall which collapsed when I patted it. We tried again, using less sand in the cement, and that wall is still standing now. Nora organised turf to be cut from a Boswell field and told us how to convert the neat Swiss rolls of grass into two pocket handkerchief lawns. She also gave us plants from her own greenhouse with directions of where they were to go; some liked the shade, others the sun, but although I followed her instructions not all survived and I filled in the gaps with bedding plants from Woolworths which were guaranteed to flower as they were already in bud.

Nora suggested we should have a tree at the end of the garden, by the gate, she said. I dug a deep hole at the agreed spot for a spindly stick labelled '*Prunus*', sifting the earth carefully over its dessicated roots and stamping in the ground as instructed, feeling it was a burial rite. Nothing would happen. That was true until life after death produced a burgeoning of pink blossom.

Nora's enjoyment in our garden increased our enjoyment. For the first time I appreciated her botanical knowledge and her deep love of flowers. When we went to Boswells for the week-end she and I made a tour of inspection of the garden and only now that I had a garden of my own could I take a genuine interest in what she said. The rockery was her greatest pride. I could never really understand why. It seemed to me to be a mass of wooden labels and very few flowers.

'I brought this back from Greece,' she explained, bowing down in front of a small leaf sprouting out of the ground which was too precious to have the grass surrounding it removed.

We visited the iris garden where every shade of iris was in bloom except the 'boring' purple, which was the only one I knew until now. We walked back to the house up the drive and Nora stopped opposite some shrub with a lengthy Latin name and said,

'I stole this from Kew,' and laughed at the expression on my face. 'I took a cutting when no-one was looking. Many of the shrubs, the rare and beautiful ones, have been filched from public gardens.'

I was shocked. 'But . . . if . . . everyone . . .' I began, but Nora had spied a crop of ground elder, and was tut-tutting under her breath.

'Sharpe must clear that away tomorrow. Dreadful stuff. I hope you will never get any of it in your garden.' Then she paused and added,

'Does it worry you that you are so much better off than Erasmus's friends?'

'Better off? We're not better off. His friends are free. They go on holidays abroad and all of them own cars. Erasmus has to travel on public transport every day.'

When I waved Erasmus goodbye from the front door each morning I always thought how noble he was, suffering the rigours of public transport. I praised him many times, wanting him to know that I appreciated the sacrifice he was making on my account. The price he paid for being married to me was having to foot-slog it along to a bus stop or a station; no whizzing off under his own power for him. Poor Erasmus.

Poor Erasmus indeed! Shortly after this conversation, in preparation for taking his raincoat to the cleaners, I emptied the pockets and discovered something which was soon to disillusion me about this noble charater. It was not a handkerchief with lipstick stains that I found, nor an incriminating love letter, but a pair of goggles. Why should he want a pair of goggles for travelling on public transport? As I tried to puzzle out the answer a suspicion slowly formed in my mind, a suspicion which he confirmed as true that night on his return from work. Without consulting me, without telling me, he had bought a motor-bicycle and secreted it in a garage on Haverstock Hill. Every day when I kissed him goodbye he let me think he was going off to catch a bus or the tube, when in fact he was walking to the garage to don his motor bike gear before riding down to UCH.

I didn't make a scene. I just asked,

'Where has the money come from?'

'The money's there.'

'Where?'

'There.'

'Our deposit account?'

'No.' He had written a cheque. Why didn't it bounce? My father's cheques often bounced, why wasn't this one returned to drawer? There seemed to be no answer forthcoming to my questions.

I opened my mouth to complain how I had been scrimping and scrounging for months to provide the baby's layette, which consisted of free gifts and dresses made from cut-price remnants when I looked at Erasmus's face and instead of releasing a flow of invective, I started to laugh. He epitomised the guilty husband. Thank goodness his clandestine assignation had only been with a motor bicycle and not with a mistress installed in a flat on Haverstock Hill. I met the 'other woman' that same evening. We went for a gentle spin around Hampstead and my resentment soon disappeared as I sat on the pillion, my arms around Erasmus's waist and the wind blowing through my hair. Nora was not so easy to placate. She pursed her lips, looked severe, until I pointed out that a motor bicycle would get him earlier to the hospital and allow him to spend longer at his work. She may not have believed what I said, but I think she was glad that I thought it was true.

I never discovered how much Erasmus's motor bicycle cost. He would have told me if I had the courage to ask, but I preferred not to know. The imaginary amount worried me nevertheless and inhibited me from spending any money on myself. I refrained from buying a maternity dress until the safety pins that kept my skirt together no longer met. Treasure Cot in Oxford Street provided me with a nasty little frock in blue-grey woollen crepe designed for someone well past child-bearing age. It had a long floppy bib in front which caught the smallest gust of wind, physiological or meteorological, and blew up, revealing the bulge underneath which it was supposed to hide.

At my request Nora accompanied me when I went to inspect a nursing home suggested by Miss Dodds. It was in

Clapham, a district new to me which on a warm spring day seemed muggy, noisy and thoroughly down at heel. My first impression of the nursing home was 'Oh, my God, have I really got to have my baby in this dump?' I expressed my doubts on the journey back but Nora could see no reason why it would not do. The matron had been a little harrassed but she seemed kind. The room which I had booked with a sense of impending doom had a nice large window looking out on the street. What was I expecting? she asked. I didn't know, and in any case I couldn't fuss because she was going to foot the bill – nine pounds for my fortnight's stay.

After lunch in Fullers we went to John Lewis to choose a pram. Nora wanted something modern, lightweight, easy to handle and close to the ground, but I yearned for the old-fashioned type of pram which I had seen uniformed nannies pushing in the park, the sort of pram that has inside an immaculate baby who will grow up to wear a coat with a velvet collar and a peaked cap. My choice cost almost double the one Nora wanted me to have and since she was paying for it I had to agree. With so much going for free I decided to streamline my needs, in order to avoid too many duplicates. I told Aunt Ruth she should be responsible for bootees, and Nora to continue to produce matinee jackets. Not the most tactful thing to do even if the intention was reasonable enough. The supply, which had been in danger of exceeding demand immediately dried up, and only Lady Darwin continued to send vests knitted on enormous needles out of wonderfully soft wool.

At the end of May, Theo gave birth to a son. Carl telephoned the news to me in a state of wild excitement, but when I visited Theo in Wimpole Street at the home of Sir Thomas Barlow and the beloved Aunt Helen her usual cheerfulness seemed forced, and with a trembling lip that looked curiously out of place on her naturally rubicund face, she explained why.

'There is something wrong with his feet. I knew there was as soon as I saw him,' she said. Talipes. Club feet. The baby asleep in his cot, so small and still and composed, had no idea what lay ahead – hospital visits, plaster casts, perhaps the surgeon's knife. My concern for Theo soon ricocheted back on to myself. What would happen if my baby was born with talipes? Genes. Dreaded genes. . . .

When we next met at Boswells, Nora and I discussed Theo's problem. Nora soon picked up my anxiety and took a rather bracing attitude, pointing out that this deformity (spine chilling word) could be cured in time, unlike her own daughter's permanent disfigurement, Joan's hare lip and cleft palate. She didn't actually voice the comparison but I felt sure that was in her mind when later she produced the correspondence dealing with the appalling events after Joan's birth. I shall never forget that afternoon, with Nora reading me those distressing letters in the same unemotional voice, the same neutral tone that she always adopted for reading out loud, Jane Austen or Walter Scott in the evening, after dinner. And Why? Was this supposed to be light entertainment for me while I rested on the sofa or something she had to prove, something she must get off her chest? I didn't understand then and I don't understand now – unless Nora was behaving as I often behave myself, trying to ward off adversity by preparing for it.

8

At the end of June we cleaned up the cottage in readiness for a tenant who was going to rent it from us while we were away. We had planned this months ahead, the date was fixed and unchangeable as the date of birth on the pink card. Everything fitted perfectly – Erasmus's midwifery course coinciding with my parents' holiday at Wootton on the Isle of Wight. While he was in residence at the hospital I would stay with them and be thoroughly spoilt.

Part of me felt sad that a stranger was going to sit on the sofa with the yellow piping and bask in the instant sunshine of the striped curtains, but it was a case of needs must. This was the last lap – in four weeks time the baby would be born and our troubles over.

Nora lent us the car for the journey to the Isle of Wight. We spent a tender, tearful night in a guest house before Erasmus handed me over to my parents in the morning. From now on every whim was satisfied, and I had whims galore. The rumblings of war could not compete with my latest symptom which dominated the conversation at every meal. My father read the *News Chronicle* at breakfast and tried to hide his anxiety behind a smile, because his cherished daughter must not be worried. In her condition she must not be allowed to see the editor's comment that we might soon get back in this country the armaments Britain sold to Germany earlier in the year. I read it, of course, and thought 'how witty!' Nothing more. It was as though the amniotic fluid protecting the baby from the outside world was protecting me, too.

Sunny, rose-scented days passed peacefully but I could not sleep during the long, warm nights. In my bed beside the open window I lay awake, counting the shooting stars and cuddling my huge stomach, content to feel luscious and ripe, until news reached me that Aunt Helen was giving a dance at her London house. It was in aid of some worthy cause which Erasmus felt duty bound to support. Then I was furious.

Here was I, stuck down in the back of beyond, big and ugly, with nothing to do but wait for the birth of my baby which according to Miss Dodds' calculations was not due for another three weeks while *MY* husband was taking time off from his precious work to enjoy himself with all those slim and gorgeous girls. Incensed with jealous brain burning I fought back with the only available means and went into labour, timing the first pains to begin at the hour the dance was due to start.

My parents thought the pains were just a hoax, a subtle way of attracting attention to myself, until unable to lie still in bed I got up on all fours, groaning with every contraction, which sent my father scurrying to the nearest telephone kiosk, badgering the operator for medical help. A midwife arrived, a veritable Mrs Gamp, who after rinsing her hands in a bowl filled with water from the kitchen kettle, examined me internally by the flickering light of a candle and announced I was well and truly in labour, although the birth was not imminent yet.

Somehow, somewhere, during that crazy, chaotic night I visited a doctor who booked me into a private room at a nursing home in Ryde. We had no car and a taxi had to be found. Every plan required another trip up the hill to the telephone box, in which my father spent much of the night waiting for Erasmus to ring for the latest news of the rapidly changing events. Even the man on the telephone exchange became involved. He listened in to the conversation, adding his comments at the end.

When the taxi arrived Tam and Nan, the au pair who became his wife forty years later but that's another story –went with me on the long, dark drive to Ryde. My brother, sitting on the back seat, kept his hands on my shoulders to steady me when the car rounded a sharp corner or hit a bump in the road. My room in the nursing home was a great improvement on the one in London; a frilly cot beside my bed sent me into a delirium of excitement as though this was all the Christmasses and birthdays rolled into one, which perhaps explains why the doctor injected morphia into my arm. After being wafted away into a dreamless sleep I awoke pain free and determined to return to London as soon as I could. I got dressed in the few clothes I had hastily put on the night before. No knickers, no stockings and my wedding ring missing too, but never mind, today I would see my husband again and that mattered more than anything else in the whole world.

The sunlight was flittering through the curtains as I went downstairs calling 'Nurse'. No-one came. I walked along a corridor and pushed open a door where a couple of nurses sitting in arm chairs were too deep in magazines to notice me until I said,

'I am going back to London, please may I use the phone?'

They jumped to their feet and in a flustered protest called Sister, who, equally put out, summoned Matron from her bed.

'You could harm the baby,' they chorused. Nothing anyone said could alter my determination to leave on the first boat. If I could do that, we, the baby and I, would be all right.

Reluctantly they granted me permission to use the phone. It was five o'clock in the morning and there was no reason to suppose my father would be waiting in the phone box for the telephone to ring, but when I dialled the number there he was, at the end of the line, ready to lift the receiver at the very first ping.

Tam, Nan and I caught the eight o'clock boat across the water. Tam, very much in love with Nan, a love that was to endure forty years without seeing her – but that belongs to the other story –devoted all his attention to me. He extracted a promise from the Captain that if necessary the boat would turn round and go back. He followed me into the ladies' cloakroom and stood outside the lavatory door, shouting 'Are you all right?' every few seconds.

On the crowded holiday train my large bulk ensured me a corner seat. A lady sitting opposite me asked,

'When are you expecting the baby, my dear?'

'Today,' I replied, 'I am in labour now.'

With a shocked 'Oh,' she shifted along the seat and said,

'Put your feet up here, and bear down.' Tam intervened, 'Don't you dare,' he said, 'I don't want you giving birth on the train even if the Southern Railway guarantee to pay for the confinement if you do.'

When we drew in at Waterloo station I was already half out of the carriage door before the train had properly stopped and

Tam, with a look of despair, watched me run the length of the platform into Erasmus's arms.

'Are you all right?' Erasmus asked in stricken tones. I assured him I had never felt better in my life. The joy at being with him again reduced my pains to a mere niggle in the back. He was visibly suffering more than I was. An ambulance parked near the barrier had caused him major distress. He assumed it was waiting for me and for once the Barlow imagination had got out of control; it took several minutes for him to absorb the fact that it was waiting for someone else.

Aunt Helen drove us to the nursing home where the matron, seeming even more harrassed than before, made no attempt to welcome us. I was not expected to arrive until the end of the week at the very earliest. If everthing wasn't as it should be I had no-one to blame but myself. They were also short-staffed, I discovered, and there were other disadvantages too – road works were being carried on outside my window. The pneumatic drill juddered a frantic ostinato to that long day as I waited on my own for the arrival of Miss Dodds.

She had told me it wouldn't be a picnic but that wasn't true; it *was* exactly like a picnic, a picnic when everything goes wrong –when it rains and the midges bite and the corkscrew has been left behind. The inadequacies of the nursing home soon became apparent. The minute apparatus failed to function until Erasmus paid an opportune visit and successfully applied a spanner to its works. There was also a crisis about the steriliser and a moment of humour too when I said,

'Miss Dodds I advise forceps.'

That caused a laugh, but her main concern seemed to be for Erasmus, whom she kept referring to as 'that poor boy;' What that poor boy must be suffering . . . oh dear . . . oh dear . . . that poor boy must be put out of his agony straight away. The last stages of my labour ceased to be a picnic in the rain and became an arduous tennis match. My formidable opponent always won the lengthy rallies until just before midnight I served an ace and the umpire declared the game, set, and match to be mine. There was real joy in Miss Dodds' voice as she said,

'It's a boy.'

The next day every muscle in my body ached and euphoria took the edge off anxiety that the first feed had been a non-event with the baby grimacing as the ham-handed nurse pushed his face against my breast.

'He doesn't want to suck,' she said, stating the obvious and implying it was my fault. Every other baby in the nursery put to the breast for ten minutes each side thrived. Why couldn't he? He fretted and cried between feeds and produced frequent green motions. He was losing weight at such a speed that I feared he would soon disappear altogether.

Letters, telegrams and bouquets of flowers poured in and then the visitors arrived.

They came at all hours and after admiring the baby made conflicting claims as to which side of the family his features belonged. Margaret Keynes had no doubts about the origin of this particular species. Bearing her gift of a matinee jacket she approached the cot reverently and on bended knee – well, almost on bended knee, intoned,

'Another Darwin has been born.'

Sir Thomas Barlow, now in his ninety-fifth year, arrived in the middle of a feed when I was trying to appear calm but feeling increasingly distraught that my ample milk supply was doing the baby so little good. He took in the true situation at one myopic glance and pride in his great grandson changed to pratical concern. After studying the depressing weight chart he bent low over me, his beard tickling my bare bosom, and listened to the baby suck. He asked a few qustions about the colour and frequency of what he termed 'stools' and then without further to-do suggested a nurse, a properly trained nurse, should be brought in from outside to take charge.

Nurse Poole arrived next morning. A strange little hobgoblin with pebble specs and bandy legs, a devoted disciple of Truby King, whose theories she immediately wanted to put into practice. The cot must be moved over to the open window in a current of fresh air which was somehow different from the draught under the door that needed a screen to prevent it from reaching the baby. Regular feeding every four hours, of course, but where were the scales? A baby with these alarming symptoms must be test fed. Having expressed her horror to the wilting matron she revealed the name of a baby food manufacturer who would supply this essential piece of equipment free of charge. To satisfy her obsessive need to record a weight change to the last quarter of an ounce Erasmus must take time off work and travel down to the East End and collect an enormous pair of scales which became my constant companion for the next few months.

In spite of her strange appearance, Nurse Poole commanded respect in the nursing home. Quoting from the Truby King manual, 'Feeding and Care of the Baby', she accused the ineffectual staff of over-feeding the baby by insisting on a ten-minute suck at each breast.

'Every bit as dangerous as under-feeding,' she said – page twenty-nine, paragraph two. The first test feed showed that Jeremy took his full Truby King ration in four minutes, and once that was established I stopped weeping with despair and started weeping with joy at the upward curve on the weight chart and that most beautiful of sights, a sight beyond compare – a bright yellow, sweet-smelling motion in his nappy,

'We might easily have lost him', the great grandfather remarked later. Nora, as was often the case with opinions expressed by her father-in-law, did not agree. She thought the cause was due to what happened before the birth rather than any mismanagement of the nursing home.

'The birth of Jeremy,' she wrote to Horace (he showed me the letter) 'was a thoroughly Black family affair, which might well have ended in tragedy.' When the nursing home closed down the following month I wondered if Sir Thomas had played a part in its demise. Even at his great age he was still a very influential figure in the medical world.

One night, while I was still in the nursing home, there was a practice black-out in London. Curtains had to be kept tightly drawn while search lights scanned the skies for imaginary enemy aircraft. I was far too involved with the baby, this new extension of myself whose dominating presence I had been quite unprepared for, to take any notice of what was happening outside my room. My own private nurse, (yes, how I enjoyed that privilege bought with Barlow money) let slip a word or two about the likelihood of war. I never took the possibility seriously until after my return to Boswells when the headlines in the newspapers grew so large that they could no longer be ignored. Leaves cancelled, parliament recalled,

Stalin's non-aggression pact signed with Germany all pointed to one conclusion.

'There is going to be a war,' I said to Aunt Helen when she came bustling through the door on to the verandah where I sat reading *The Times.*

Surprised by this news flash coming from such an unlikely source as myself who normally never said anything that wasn't appertaining to the baby, she stopped in her tracks and exclaimed 'Oh dear, is there really?' and then after reading the headlines over my shoulder she agreed with what I had said. 'There *is* going to be a war,' she repeated. We looked at each other in silence while a wood pigeon cooed peace through the summer garden. Then she went off to do something useful, pick plums or visit one of the tenants, and I turned my mind to the silliest of things – whether I was slim enough to justify buying a pair of trousers to take with me on holiday.

Nora had rented a school near Robin Hood's Bay and invited several friends to dilute the family, or as she often said, 'leaven the dough'. They left by car and we were to join them if the political situation didn't worsen, a phrase which became increasingly familiar throughout that month of August. We very much wanted to join the house party, and dismissing the newspaper reports as exaggerated outpourings of the silly season we left Boswells on August the twenty-seventh to travel north by train, the whole of a first class compartment being occupied by Erasmus, myself, Nurse Poole, the baby in his carry-cot and the cumbersome scales. Test feeding still prevailed.

The school, Filing Hall, offered few comforts and we had to fit in the best that we could. A large number of guests responded to Nora's generous open invitation to come and stay and the party included a German Jewish refugee and a Nazi from Düsseldorf. Contrary to expectations these two got on very well. Every evening while we all played raucous card games round the table they sat in a huddle discussing the latest news on the wireless.

On the historic morning of September the first we walked down to the beach across the fields. After a quick dip in the cold sea we warmed up by playing French and English on the sand. We gave the game a contemporary touch by calling it

Germans and English. There is a photograph of us – Horace, Hilda, Clare Cornford, Mark Pryor myself and Gill – striding home through the long grass and it is difficult to reconcile that happy, smiling, carefree group with the invasion of Poland. Mrs Mason, the cook, broke the news to us as soon as we entered the house; her natural relish in disaster was only partially satisfied. She still had room for pleasure in the evacuation plans, and had the kitchen radio turned up full blast for the rest of the day.

Now that what we had dreaded happening had actually happened, we felt a kind of relief which was close to exhilaration and lunch was a cheerful chattering meal with only Nora looking utterly shattered at the end of the table.

'You've no idea what it's going to be like,' she said, almost in tears.

She imagined the next war would have the same slow, grinding misery as the last one, in which her brother and brother-in-law had been killed, while we, influenced by H G Wells *The Shape of Things to Come* assumed instant bombing and devastation which somehow or other we would survive – such is the optimism of youth.

An urge to return to base infected us all apart from the blond, blue eyed Aryan god who made it clear that he wanted to be interned in England and play tennis for the duration of the war. A brusque telephone call from Germany demanding his patriotic presence back in the Vaterland put an end to this dream. It was a very sulky Nazi who sat beside the resigned Jewish refugee in the back of the car when we drove them to Scarborough to fulfil the latest regulations and register with the police.

That night black out came into force, and as we had no curtains in our bedroom, packing had to be done groping in the dark. Outside, distant rumbling and flashing lights from a thunderstorm could easily be mistaken for a battle out at sea. The only reading matter in our room was a book about the damage done in the Great War by enemy guns firing at the east coast, and at any moment I feared Filing Hall would become like one of the photographs I had seen.

In the half-light of early morning we packed up the car with Jeremy in his carry-cot, the scales and all the baby paraphenalia occupying the back seat. Why we borrowed the car I don't know, neither have I any idea of how Nora got home. It was all part of the emergency planning that went on until midnight and left me short of sleep, so that I was hardly aware of saying goodbye to the stalwart Nurse Poole. For some reason it was decided she should travel back with Mark Pryor, but they did not get very far. Their car skidded into the ditch half way up the drive and that was the last I saw of her – keeling over, surounded by luggage, unperturbed, as though this was all part of her day's work.

Our stops on the way home were ruled by the Truby King routine. Scales were heaved in and out of the car for a test feed at the edge of the road, another in a hotel cloakroom; by two o'clock, thank goodness, we had reached Boswells and were back in occupation of our bedroom at the end of the corridor.

The garden was more beautiful than I had ever seen it before or since with the herbaceous border at its peak glowing in the sunshine; butterflies fluttered round the michaelmas daisies and the red hot pokers really looked red hot. In the familiar surroundings with so many happy associations war lost its inevitability. Perhaps this would just be another Munich crisis, the same as the year before; some last minute compromise would be pulled out of the hat. When on the nine o'clock news Greenwood was reported as saying 'the door is still ajar' I felt there was real hope and went to bed clutching that last straw.

In the small hours shrill wailing punctured my sleep and I awoke with a jolt, thinking it was the siren, unable to believe that the urgent sound came from my baby, demanding to be fed while it was still dark. He must wait until six o'clock. Even if the whole household suffered, Truby King's first commandment must be obeyed: 'Thou shalt not pick up a baby between feeds.'

Thanks to Jeremy and Chamberlain no-one slept very well that night and a bleary-eyed family gathered round the radio in the drawing room to listen to the important statement that the Prime Minister was to broadcast from Downing Street at eleven o'clock. Nora sat at her bureau; Alan walked restlessly round the room; grey-faced shapes slumped in chairs and I leaned against the door with a pail of washed nappies in my hand. Outside, the sun shone, and the birds sang; through the hall wafted the smell of breakfast kedgeree, giving a semblance of a normal Sunday morning until Neville Chamberlain in level tones declared,

'This country is now at war with Germany.'

No-one spoke. There was nothing to say. Nora picked up her pen and continued writing her letter. Alan retreated to his compost heap. I carried my washing out into the yard and hung it up on the line, feeling resentful and angry, as though the war was a private vendetta against myself. The happiness I had just been able to touch was going to be snatched away by events outside my control.

In the glorious autumnal sunshine Nora and I walked up the path between the sun-soaked herbaceous borders and sat down on the seat to discuss immediate plans.

'You mustn't return to London,' Nora said, 'it wouldn't be safe.' And at that moment the bland security of the soft warm day was torn in shreds by the siren's screech. The first air-raid warning. Less than half an hour after the declaration of war. This was what H G Wells predicted . I ran down the path; nightmare legs refused to move quickly across the lawn, which had become a vast expanse of green, double its normal length from the verandah where Jeremy lay fast asleep in his pram. I longed to gather him up in my arms, carry him off to a safe place, into a cupboard, under the stairs, but no, it was between feeds and Truby King said . . . I hesitated with my hand on the pram and as I waited the all clear sounded, not the undulating panic of the alarm but a single note, like a shaft of sunlight breaking through the stormy clouds of fear. We all sighed with relief, laughed a little awkwardly as though we had been taken in by a practical joke and agreed it had been just a false alarm.

When the verandah bell clanged to bring Alan in from the compost heap and then the gong boomed for lunch it seemed impossible to believe in Neville Chamberlain's announcement two hours before. I expected some signs of crisis but there in the dining room parlourmaids stood with their backs to the sideboard ready to hand round plates of roast beef and yorkshire pudding. I remembered the photographs the Muller family had shown me of themselves – gaunt and hollow-cheeked after the First World War and I tried to imagine the plump faces round the table looking undernourished. At that first wartime lunch there was chocolate mousse for pudding, decorated with angelica, glace cherries and swirls of cream. I gazed at it in wonderment, unable to reconcile such indulgence with the country being at war. I expected austerity to start straight away.

Evacuees arrived the following week and after two nights in the attic bedrooms and meals in the servants' hall they went back to the East End of London complaining they couldn't stand the quiet. Their rooms were quickly occupied by two of the Wimpole Street staff; Aunt Helen's lady's maid, whom she addressed as Irving as though she was a man, and the cook, who was a spinster but had the gratuitous title of Mrs before her name. Susan Butson's hymn singing increased as tension mounted behind the green baize door. Our appropriating a stray kitten only added weight to the cross Susan had to bear. We called the kitten 'Poland' and thoroughly enjoyed it until Susan came to us with wispy hair and lengthened face to complain that the inner sanctum of her temple had not only been invaded but defiled.

'Poland has done a mess in the airing cupboard,' she said.

The kitten must go. We found another home for it at once. We grovelled and apologised, but nothing that we did or said could compensate for the damage done. 'Abide With Me' changed to a belligerent 'Onward Christian Soldiers, marching as to war. . . .'

Nora had taught me the necessity of saying 'good morning' to the servants and what had previously been an agony was now a conditioned reflex. But after the kitten episode I dreaded meeting Susan because she now behaved as I had done. Slinking past me with head bent she never acknowledged my greeting and made me feel I didn't exist.

The airing cupboard remained a sensitive area. Everything had to be put in a special place, the baby's napkins in particular had to be aired at maximum distance from the sacrosanct sheets and pillowcases used by 'her ladyship'. The battleground extended to the cubby hole at the end of the passage where Susan dictated a routine to be followed after my washing the baby's clothes which seemed to me, coming from a haphazard Irish household, both aggressive and mad. Bowls must be wiped inside and out and stacked in a certain order; the bucket must be left under the sink, upside down, and the scrubbing brush, her major fetish, for the sake of its rapidly diminishing bristles must never be allowed to lie face downward on the draining board but put on its side, against the packet of soap flakes which she checked every day to ensure I hadn't been too extravagant with its contents.

I did my best to comply with her wishes. I even persuaded myself there was a lot of worthwhile common sense in what she said. But no sooner had I mastered one hurdle than another cropped up to take its place. Now it was the way we always woke her up at night because of the noise we made when closing our bedroom door. I tip-toed up and down the passage, turning the door handle slowly and releasing it with care, doing everything I could to ensure she was not disturbed, but it was a lone battle. Erasmus refused to cooperate. Susan had been his nanny and his resentment against her treatment of him in those nursery days remained.

'She always forced me to eat up my sago pudding,' he said, banging the bedroom door last thing at night.

I never knew whether these petty skirmishes remained isolated at our end of the house. I can hardly believe Susan lost an opportunity to drop hints, hints as dark as the shadows under her eyes, about our inconsiderate behaviour, but Nora must have decided to let us fight it out on our own rather than interfere, and after all, anything Susan said would, in those days, be classed as 'servant talk' – something to be ignored. So the day to day feuds continued unabated with me doing everything I could to keep the peace and Erasmus welcoming any chance to pay off old scores.

When Theo arrived with her baby, Robert, Susan put her through the initiation ceremony in the housemaid's cupboard. Unlike me, Theo found the fuss over buckets, bowls and scrubbing brush very amusing, and her light-hearted attitude encouraged me to see the funny side. I stopped being so sulkily oppressed by what we now called Susan's reign of terror. Together we fed our babies in the bathroom, sitting as closely as we could to the warm pipes. Our bedrooms were always very chilly and the living-rooms were out of bounds for regurgitating infants and bare breasts.

Saving fuel, a wartime necessity, justified Nora's inclination to keep the house at an uncomfortably low temperature. Aunt

Helen tried to solve the heating problem by wrapping coal dust in sheets of newspaper, a useful tip she had read in a magazine, but the parcels disintegrated before reaching the grate, covering the Persian carpets with soot, and so the experiment was never tried again.

We went potato picking in the fields, why I don't know, no farm workers had yet been called up, but the desire to get going with the war effort was strong. We wanted to do our bit even if there was nothing to do but wait. The first casualty in our midst was Joey, Aunt Helen's beloved mare. A patriotic sacrifice. She could no longer justify her keep. Her death was never mentioned and any emotion Aunt Helen felt at the loss she locked inside herself, an example of admirable control.

Part of University College Hospital moved out to Hemel Hempstead to await the casualties from air raids on London which were expected to happen straight away, but didn't. Erasmus was obliged to spend several nights there each week and although I hated him being away I didn't dare grumble because it was all part of the war effort, and preferable to his being in London, which at any moment the Luftwaffe might attack. Theo's companionship was a great boon. We gossiped while we fed our babies, gossiped after they had been put down in their prams and went on gossiping while we washed the nappies, lowering our voices if anyone came near. What an infuriating couple we must have been!

'If we didn't have you here we'd have to try our luck again with evacuees,' Nora said, not just once but several times, as though she was trying to reassure herself that there was a worse alternative to us.

Every morning Nora went into the kitchen and had a session with the cook. The menu for the day was written down on a slate, with different food for the servants' hall, a slightly inferior version of what was being prepared for us in the dining-room. In spite of the numbers in the house, standards never dropped, and the gong boomed us all into meals four times a day, with Nora always calm at the head of the table. She only showed irritation with her husband if he uncorked another bottle of wine when she thought he had already drunk enough.

The arrival of Geoffrey Keynes in our midst added tone to the enforced selection of guests. He was stationed at Halton

Camp and brought with him his orderly, a podgy young man with rounded cheeks and buttocks to match, whom Nora instantly disliked. Geoffrey, resplendent as a group captain, reminded me of the advertisement for Black Magic chocolates. He looked like the dapper young man who since the outbreak of war had exchanged his tennis flannels and blazer for an officer's uniform. They had the same clipped moustache, the same knife-edge creases to their trousers, the same handsome profile beneath the peaked cap; the only thing Geoffrey lacked was the glamorous young lady on whom the chocolates were to work their magic.

We joked about Geoffrey behind his back. 'Geoffrey and his boy', that pink, plump batman, gave ample scope for Carl's malicious wit. Even Nora enjoyed a little Geoffrey baiting. She noticed that his sun-tan wasn't fading now that the days turned autumnal and cold. He must have a sunlamp secreted in his bedroom – how else could that bronze complexion be explained? Nora called it a wanton piece of vanity, of which she thoroughly disapproved. We larked around with Geoffrey's gold-braided cap hanging on a peg in the front lobby; we put it on each other's heads, laughed at ourselves in the mirror and photographed Jeremy wearing it falling over his eyes.

Intellectually Geoffrey could have made mincemeat of us all, but he never sank so low as to do that. He always remained tolerant and polite, even when I challenged him on an issue particularly close to his heart. The confrontation took place in the hall, where Geoffrey stood, immaculate in his well pressed uniform, smooth grey head bent lovingly over a book he had taken from the shelf. Since there was no-one else around at that moment to receive the emotion he felt the need to express, he addressed himself to me,

'What a joy it is to read a book when it is a first edition and so exquisitely bound,' he said.

Irritated by his rapturous tone, I questioned his remark.

'Surely what's important is not the binding of a book but what's inside. I prefer my books imbued with my own personality, the more dog-eared, underlined and covered with notes in the margin, the better,' I said.

Geoffrey's tolerant smile retracted at such sacrilege and his expressive nostrils drew up as though encountering an unpleasant smell; even his artificial tan sallowed. He didn't speak to me again until dinner, when with a severe look across the table he said,

'Do you think we might possibly be allowed one meal when the conversation isn't about babies?' *Touché.*

The phoney war produced its own brand of tension. With so many of us staying in the house for apparently so little reason we became caricatures of ourselves in order to retain our true identity. Geoffrey's fastidiousness increased until his nose was forever wrinkling in disdain. Aunt Helen held forth on the lowering of moral standards. Not just in others but in herself as well. She had been shocked by her own reaction to the sight of a heap of sticks from a broken down fence at the edge of the road.

'I had every intention of piling those sticks into the boot of my car,' she confessed, 'until I realised they must be someone else's property and what I was about to do was tantamount to stealing.'

Alan, usually monosyllabic, now became completely silent, while Nora, less willing to suffer fools gladly, snubbed me soundly for boasting that both my brothers were conscientious objectors.

'They're leaving other people to do the dirty work,' she snapped.

I pointed out that Tam had volunteered for the fire brigade in the East End of London on the day war broke out and Teedie refused a cushy job at the Ministry of Information which, had he accepted it, would have saved him a grilling at a tribunal. If they deserved any praise for sticking to their principles, they didn't get it.

And what about Horace, I thought, remembering the subterranean flurry over his future career and the ripples of relief when a decision was reached that he should go up to Cambridge rather than join the army.

'The Bobba says Horace would make a much better doctor than a soldier,' Nora said, quoting Horace's house-master at Winchester for whom she had great respect. There had been no talk of other people doing the dirty work then.

Yes, we were all showing signs of strain from nothing happening. When something did happen and Joan developed an eye complaint there seemed to be little sympathy available, apart from Geoffrey, who recognised the seriousness of her condition. Joan had just began work at a children's home evacuated from London to the Manor House in Wendover and was greatly appreciated by the staff. How tiresome of her to get ill at this moment! Nora appeared irritably concerned and it was Geoffrey who volunteered to fix an appointment at a London hospital for Joan to see one of the world experts on this rare disease.

9

By the middle of October we could almost believe in the rumour that the war would be over by Christmas without any bombs being dropped. A drift back to towns began. Hilda and Horace had already gone off to their universities (Bangor and Cambridge) and Andrew was at medical school in London. The numbers round the table diminished further when Aunt Helen took her father back to number ten Wimpole Street and Theo and Carl returned with Robert to their house in Kensington. University College had been evacuated to Hemel Hempstead and once Erasmus was settled there he found rooms for us all in a vicarage on the outskirts of the town. Geoffrey was left alone, with only Nora and Joan for company. We noticed that he looked rather miserable when we said goodbye.

'Not enough people to admire him, that's why,' Erasmus said. 'He'll be all right when the house fills up at weekends.'

I turned round to give a final wave from the car but he'd already gone indoors. For some inexplicable reason we both felt responsible for his welfare.

The vicarage was a typically unmanageable Victorian building with a vicar and his wife too busy being Christian outside the house to turn it into a home. We decorated the attic bedroom to make it look like a nursery, with a teddy bear frieze and brightly striped curtains, but the small sitting-room failed to inspire us. It remained a slum. The blue paper covering the windows to help the blackout gave the impression of permanent fine weather outside.

We shared the kitchen and bathroom with another young married couple, who being childless had never heard of Truby King. They thought my obsession of living by the clock ridiculous, especially if in any way it inconvenienced them. When I found the bathroom occupied at the time Jeremy was due to be washed a stormy scene ensued, with my banging on the door and a lot of splashing and running water answering back.

There was a preparatory school next door, where every day Erasmus and I went round to share for very little cost the midday meal with a host of grey flannelled little boys.

That ended when somehow or other we acquired a first class cook who appeared every morning to prepare us a most delicious lunch. I cannot recall what she looked like or her name. I only remember her Wienerschinetzel which we were eating when news came through over the wireless that Russia had invaded Finland.

Having made a nursery for Jeremy in the vicarage we were soon doing the same again in a cottage at Piccott's end. we moved into this small straggling village, three miles from Hemel Hempstead when the snow was deep on the ground, and were so delighted at having a place of our own that frozen pipes and damp bedding did not matter at all.

A touching scene took place in the cottage opposite shortly after we arrived. It should have been in a frame with the title underneath 'A soldier's farewell'. A young man in khaki with kitbag slung over his shoulder was saying goodbye to his mother, who stood at the garden gate surrounded by snow. She was speaking to him eagerly, last words of advice perhaps, or wishing him good luck – I shall never know what she said, but suddenly, as though he had had enough, he opened wide his arms and gathered her into an embrace, his bulky trench coat shielding her from my view. When they separated he marched off quickly down the frozen road without looking back at the sad figure who lifted her apron to her face to weep away the tears.

One day Erasmus invited his boss home to tea. Married students were still a frowned-upon rarity and Dermot Macarthy arrived expecting to be entertained alone in some scruffy lodging. He didn't try to conceal his pleasure at finding his student with a wife and baby living in a picturesque cottage. As the clock struck six, Truby King asserted himself, up went my jersey, out came my breast and I won the paediatrician's approval by feeding Jeremy while carrying on the conversation. When it was time to go Dermot asked if he could borrow my son to show his students what a seven months old baby should be like. A suggestion not to be taken seriously, but a compliment nevertheless.

When Jeremy had to have new clothes I rejected the traditional blue in favour of dark checks and brightly spotted materials. With the help of a paper pattern I cut out rompers on the school room table when we went to Boswells for the week-end. They seemed much more complicated than the dresses I had lovingly hand-stitched for his layette, and the ancient sewing machine which Susan used to mend the sheets, putting sides to middle, came to my rescue over the flat seams that the instructions demanded. Everything lasted longer than I expected and rather than leave the rompers unfinished I took the sewing machine back with me to Piccott's End to complete my work. It never entered my head to ask permission or let anyone know. That was how we behaved in my family, where all our possessions were pooled. To object to something suddenly missing from one's room was considered very materialistic, worthy of a lecture from my mother. In the Barlow family it was the other way round. Nora could scarcely contain her irritation over the phone when she reported Susan's search for the sewing maching. Only after hunting high and low through Boswells had they come to the conclusion that I was guilty of removing it. A total lack of respect for another person's property. Oh dear! Striving to bridge the abyss of the conflicting values of the two families I felt guilty and innocent at the same time.

From now on I shunned the sewing machine. It sulked under its case until we next went to Boswells for the weekend. In a bid for independence I hired a 'Singer' from a shop in Hemel Hempstead and that same evening, Erasmus, after a trip to London, brought me back a 'Jones'. We sat either end of the table demonstrating the virtues of our rival machines. The 'Jones' won. An excellent choice which gave marathon service for the next twenty-five years when a modern version replaced it, no better than the original make. Progress doesn't necessarily advance improvement.

When the snow thawed our living-room was flooded with a foot of water and every morning a fresh crop of fungi appeared along the wainscoting with the same determination that the bulbs outside pushed up through the frozen earth. Warmer weather brought renewed hope that the war would be over soon. Both sides had complete faith in their own impenetrable fortresses, the Siegfried and Maginot lines, but this stalemate couldn't go on for ever; a compromise had to be reached soon.

The next stage of his career Erasmus had to be in London which, in this rush of optimism, we thought was now safe. After packing up our things we left the landlord to his dry rot and returned to Hampstead and our love nest in Willow Road.

I opened the front door, impatient to embrace my home, to put my arms round each room and kiss every piece of furniture, but a stagnant stench, like bad breath, made me draw back.

'What's wrong?' Erasmus asked.

'Everything.' I pointed to the scratches up the wall, the stained stair carpet, the cigarette burn on the telephone table. And we were still only in the hall. The other rooms told the same story. The refugees, friends of my sister, had not fulfilled their side of the bargain and looked after the place in return for living there rent free.

'How can anyone behave like that?' I complained to my mother, laying myself wide open for a lecture on being materialistic and selfish.

I turned to Nora for understanding. The sympathy was there, but embedded in the sympathy lay a message for me,

'I know exactly what you mean,' she said, 'it's dreadful when people have no respect for someone else's property.'

Soon the housewife in me, that little woman in a frilly apron who wanted to have everything nice, suffered yet another knock. Spinach spattered the room, spotting the walls and staining the newly cleaned carpets as Jeremy resisted my half hearted attempts at weaning. One day I sieved vegetables and made a semolina pudding and the next day, unable to face another struggle, allowed him a lengthy suck at my breasts. The house was littered with half-chewed Bickypegs, my nipples sore from his recently cut teeth. I began to wonder if he would still need breast feeding by the time he went to school, and that might well have been the case if Nora hadn't stepped in with a solution.

'Go away for a few days holiday,' she said, 'and leave the weaning to me. I know I can manage it perfectly well with

Susan's help.'

We decided to explore Dorset on the motorbike, travelling
light with only a rucksack. I packed Jeremy's clothes, wrote
out a list of instructions for his routine and said goodbye to
him at Boswells with a tearful attempt at Barlow control. By
the time we met again, the world had seen three changes. My
bust had shrunk from a milky thirty-six to an arid thirty-two,
the carefully cultivated curl on the top of Jeremy's head had
disappeared and Hitler had invaded the Low Countries.

My hormones tried their hardest to spoil our brief time
together. On the first night we searched Lulworth in the black-
out for the local GP. He lived in a terraced house and after
knocking several times at his front door a window on the first
floor shot up and a fractious voice demanded,

'What's the matter?'

Every inhabitant in that silent street must have been aware
of my symptoms when I shouted back,

'High temperature and painful, swollen breasts.'

A grumpy doctor in his dressing-gown gave me a dose of
belladonna and a piece of his mind.

'What in heaven's name did you think you were doing with
such a brutal method of weaning?' he asked. 'It can't have
done the baby much good and it certainly has done you
harm.'

He waived aside our offer to pay for the treatment and the
inconvenience caused. All he wanted to do was to go back
to sleep.

We spent a couple of languid days gazing at the sea through
barbed wire and then with our mission accomplished we started on our journey home. But we left finding accommodation
for the last night too late and had to accept a very narrow bed
in a jerry-built bungalow on the main road. In the morning I
was woken up by the unmistakeable Oxford accent of Alvar
Liddel on the other side of the paper thin wall. He announced
over the radio that the Germans had attacked through the
Ardennes. Suddenly the Maginot line had ceased to exist.

The phoney war was over and momentarily British reserve
disappeared. When we stopped at traffic lights, car windows
wound down and excited faces appeared, eager to discuss the

news. People who normally would never speak to a stranger were, on this frenetic morning of sunshine and crisis, eager to exchange words. The young man at a garage where we filled up with petrol surpassed himself with the nauseating jingo left over from the Great War.

When we arrived and found Nora calm and smiling with Jeremy in her arms, Boswells seemed to be cut off from the turmoil of the topsy-turvy world at the end of the drive. I clasped him to my flat chest and held him there while he struggled to get free. He looked different and for a few seconds I couldn't think why. He was wearing the familiar red and white spotted rompers and his podgy arms and legs were the same, but something had changed. No. I couldn't pretend that he had been suffering, if anything he looked more serene; and then I noticed his shining, freshly washed hair. How flat it lay against his head! The sausage curl, which every morning I had wound so lovingly round my finger, had gone, and there was no hope of bringing it back because a fringe had been cut in an uncompromising straight line above his eyebrows.

The curl must have offended Nora for all the months it was there. Probably it fell into the same category as charm, Tchaikovsky and variegated leaves which Darwins despise. I never mentioned how much I minded what she had done but resentment showed on my face which Nora mistook for jealously. Years later Nora still remembered this incident.

'I could see you were upset,' she said, 'when Jeremy held out his arms to me.'

Our defences crumbled as Hitler advanced, one town after another captured by the Germans. The placards in London could hardly keep pace with the news. Outside Marylebone Station I read that Calais was strongly resisting but by the time I had reached the dentist in Park Cresent it had fallen and Boulogne was under attack. The dread that Boulogne would be the next channel port to go distracted me from the whirring drill and sure enough when I came out an hour later Boulogne was in enemy hands.

As the Allied troops retreated we too retreated from Hampstead to Boswells. Jeremy was now sufficiently mobile to clamber around and make his presence felt. He endeared himself to everybody until, quite suddenly, for apparently no reason at all, he took violent exception to Geoffrey's laugh. That laugh was always beautifully timed, neither too loud nor too soft, never raucously vulgar, just a gentle crescendo from lips parted wide enough to show flashing front teeth but none of the gold stoppings at the back. Geoffrey's laugh was not an infectious laugh. It was a *tour de force*, a one man show, which put the seal of approval on a joke or acknowledged the intimacy of an innuendo. Anyone else was at liberty to laugh discordantly without producing any reaction from Jeremy, but as soon as he heard Geoffrey laugh, down went his mouth and if Geoffrey didn't swallow his laugh double quick there would be the inevitable embarrassing roar.

Weekend guests sometimes included Alan's Civil Service colleagues. Bay Kilroy, Beryl Power and Evelyn Sharp arrived looking very elegant, but the elegance disappeared when they tried to combat the country house chill by putting on jerseys and cardigans over their London clothes. Alan never paid much attention to them, preferring the compost heap for company. Nora, left to do the entertaining of these high-powered professional women generally gave them some menial task – topping and tailing gooseberries or shredding currants.

I liked Beryl Power best. Bill, as she was known, always made a great fuss over Jeremy. She recited poems to him about trains going puff puff and sent him picture postcards with messages in block letters, as though he was capable of reading what she wrote.

When Margaret Mead paid a visit she was obviously Nora's special friend, unique because unlike Nora's other friends there was no family connection. She was not a cousin. Nora had been to Bali with Margaret and her husband Gregory Bateson in 1936, a brief spell of emancipation justified by an interest in anthropology. After dinner Margaret was allowed to hold forth on the behaviour of the primitive tribes she had studied. Females living together menstruated at the same time and withdrew into huts to beat themselves with nettles to relieve tension. Fascinating stuff spoiled by the flat, nasal twang in which it was delivered. Margaret always sat in the most comfortable chair, resting her head against the back and talked with her eyes closed until lulled by the sound of her own voice she fell asleep, thus depriving the rest of the company of any chance to reply.

Nora admired Margaret, there was a touch of aspiring

junior and school prefect in their relationship. When Margaret suggested a betrothal between her daughter and Nora's grandson – Cathy and Jeremy – Nora was delighted, positively flattered that Margaret wanted to forge a link between the two families even if the union was unlikely to come off.

A general exodus from London began. Theo and Robert joined us and soon afterwards Aunt Helen and her father arrived. We were often as many as fourteen round the table for meals with an age span of ninety-four years. While the great grandfather scraped away with a spoon at the pattern on his plate, mistaking it for food, Jeremy played around with the food in his bowl, trying to turn it into a pattern.

I began to feel the ambiguity of my position in Boswells. Neither a guest nor an evacuee, I resembled a ward in a Chekov play, tolerated rather than wanted. Theo was in a similar predicament. Although neither of us had enough to do we resented having to clean our own shoes when Bean cleaned the shoes of the rest of the household. After meals we were expected to clear away when everyone else filed out of the door and went into the drawing-room. If Nora saw any crumbs left under the high chair she pointed out, nicely but firmly, that we had not done our job properly. The school room had to be tidied up every evening and the toys stowed away neatly in a cupboard. I can recapture now AND understand Nora's sigh when late at night she went into the garden and saw bricks strewn over the lawn.

The war gave Aunt Helen's good works a fresh impetus and she was busier than ever. Nora, too, was doing her conventional bit with the Red Cross; any spare moments she could snatch were spent sorting the Darwin papers in preparation for editing *The Voyage of the Beagle*. We didn't know that was what she was doing. She could have been paying bills or writing letters as far as we were concerned. Compared with them, we must have seemed extremely idle. Just two lazy lumps, loath to do anything but take offence, which explains, perhaps, that mysterious afternoon when, at Aunt Helen's suggestion, Mills took us for a drive in the Rolls Royce. We sat in the back, leaning comfortably against the plush upholstery, enjoying the luxury until suddenly, on a lonely stretch of the road, the car stopped. Mills got out and opening the door

said, 'Now you can walk.' He drove off along the straight dusty
road, leaving us to trudge towards the grey speck, which eventually grew into the Rolls with Mills once again the servile
chauffeur standing beside it, ready to open the door for us to
get in.

The beautiful weather continued. The Germans penetrated
further and further into France while we sat on the sunlit lawn
admiring our babies crawl over the grass. The pigeons cooed,
the gong boomed and every evening we gathered in the
drawing-room to listen to the nine o'clock news. Alan looked
grim, Nora tired, but the conversation, when there was any
conversation, was about trivial things – the apple crop and a
swarm of bees. The retreat from Dunkirk was dismissed as a
victory rather than hailed as the miracle that it was.

Erasmus was very tied up at the hospital, often having to
sleep there and not come home for several nights. Home
being Boswells. When he did manage to get away he resented
having to talk to people and would escape up to our bedroom
to revise for his final examination. Sometimes I followed him
upstairs and sat beside the microscope testing him on his
slides but I was never sure how much this wifely act was
appreciated. I comforted myself that he would soon be Doctor Barlow and with that hurdle over we could make something of our life. Exactly what, I wasn't sure. Probably the
most intimate thing we did during those desperate summer
months was to have a bath together, but even that was
inhibited by the close proximity of Susan on the other side of
the wall. When the Germans entered Paris our whispered discussions flared up into a heated argument.

From the tap end of the bath I insisted between clenched
teeth that if Paris fell, then France would fall.

'Didn't you hear Petain's speech?' Erasmus asked, knowing
perfectly well that I had. 'The French will go on fighting even if
Paris does fall.'

'Ssssh. . . .'

Irritated by my plea to keep his voice down he spoke
louder,

'What makes you think they'll capitulate to the Germans?'

'Sssh . . . for goodness sake . . . sssh. . . .'

'Stop shushing and answer my question.'

'The French will give in because they haven't got the guts to carry on. They're too neurotic. They all went to bed too late when they were young.'

The fall of France coincided with the last day of Erasmus's examination. He heard the news a few minutes before entering the University Senate House. He was unable to clear his mind of disaster and failed to answer all the questions, which would have been quite easy if he hadn't been so distracted.

He telephoned the bad news. I blamed the fall of France and did my best to comfort him before the telephone pips intervened. Every member of the household was waiting for the examination result and each one had to be told in turn of the failure. It would have been a mistake to let them think I didn't mind, but I pretended I didn't mind too much and this was just a setback; next time he'd be sure to pass. In reality I hardly knew how to contain my disappointment. I longed to go away and cry, but where could I be sure of privacy? Susan was always patrolling the house and in the garden Geoffrey sunbathed in the nude and Alan trekked to and fro from the compost heap. I waited until Jeremy was asleep in his cot and then I skulked off to the Round Hill, rationing my tears because at dinner time I would have to meet the family again with a cheerful face.

When Horace came down from his first year at Trinity College I was surprised how much he had grown up. I was sitting on the lawn, watching Jeremy build towers out of wooden bricks, when he strode across the grass and flopped down beside me. No longer the straw-haired boy, but a handsome young man who seemed delighted to talk about anything from what was happening in the war to complicated feelings involving relationships. We played tennis on the bumpy grass court and laughed a lot while the others, the 'grown-ups', sat still and stony faced listening to the news in the drawing-room. We picked strawberries in the walled garden and dipped them in the barrel of thick cream behind the dairy maid's back.

We sat close together on the verandah in the evening, listening to the fourth Brandenburg concerto played on the EMI gramophone with its enormous horn and wooden needle – the most modern equipment in Boswells. Sometimes he would lie with his head in my lap and I would long to stroke his hair.

When one night there was an air raid warning Nora insisted we should take it seriously. Everyone trailed down to the cellar and sat perched on dusty shelves among bottles of wine. Horace and I decided this was a pointless exercise and went out into the moonlight, danced on the lawn and then made cups of cocoa, using up the milk that was meant for breakfast. We got into trouble for that. This nearly innocent relationship produced a pocket of happiness among the gloom and lasted until Horace and Erasmus had a tremendous row which Nora insisted was really over me when in fact it was the cheese scoop that caused the sudden flare up of tempers. Erasmus wanted the Stilton cheese cut flat with the knife, going round in circles, the way it was always cut at Trinity College. Horace dug into the cheese with a scoop. Suddenly they were shouting at each other and Horace turned the garden hose on Erasmus, which instead of cooling him down had the reverse effect. I don't know how they resolved the dispute but I do know that even now the words 'cheese scoop' make the three of us laugh.

Shortly after this event Nora suggested we should try to find a cottage in the vicinity. Money was somewhere there but I never knew how much or whether we were really entitled to draw on it. There was a bungalow on Cobbler's Hill which became a castle in the air for sale at five hundred pounds. My father was delighted when he heard of this possibility and suggested we should look at 'our' property together. Together – that was the last thing I wanted. He was always hoping to establish togetherness with me, his youngest child. When I was eleven years old he would have to plead before I would consent to sit beside him at the piano and play duets –Haydn's symphonies arranged for four hands. On my wedding day he wanted a sentimental moment on our own as we drove to the church. A few loving words would have satisfied him, or even just an understanding squeeze of the hand, but no, I couldn't bring myself to make even the slightest gesture, and how I regret it now!

With no inkling that this would be our last meeting I got on my bicycle with my identity card in my pocket – identity cards were obligatory now, they had to be carried wherever we went, no matter how short the journey. My father was waiting for me at the bottom of Cobbler's Hill to help me up the steep climb by pushing his bicycle as well as mine. He loved the bungalow, although 'bungalow' was a rather grandiose word for the clapboard shack which had been hastily erected after the last war.

As usual he was reluctant to let me go and as usual I only allowed him a few minutes of my time to talk. We sat under a tree. He was wearing his plus-fours and his old felt hat. Between puffs of his pipe he painted an idyllic life for us if we lived on Cobbler's Hill.

'I could cycle over to you every week-end,' he said, and my stony little heart sank at the idea. How I wish I could pretend that I said something encouraging, but I'm sure I didn't. The conversation turned to the threat of invasion which my father was convinced would never happen. Then he told me about Teedie's tribunal, making him appear like a hero, when in fact it was my father who had been the hero by attending the court and supporting his son whom he would have been proud to see in uniform. We said goodbye. I hope I kissed him. A peck on the cheek, perhaps.

When I was called to the phone the following Saturday evening I thought what an inconvenient moment for my sister to ring –surely she must have known it was almost dinner time. I had already changed into my long sleeved silk dress and and tied a ribbon round my hair. I caught whiffs of roast chicken as I ran down the back stairs to the study where Geoffrey sat at his desk, too deep in his work to acknowledge my apology for disturbing him.

I didn't recognise my sister's voice. She sounded different. She broke the news to me without any preamble to soften the blow. Not that the blow could be softened. My father was dead. He dropped dead from a heart attack on a bus after giving up his seat to a passenger. I felt as though a huge oak tree had crashed against my window. I felt a knife had been stuck in my chest. Deep in my chest. I doubled up with pain and would have fallen to the ground if Geoffrey's arms hadn't engulfed me. He tried to comfort me but I broke away and tore down the corridor screaming that my father had always had to work too hard. Thousands and thousands of words dictated every day to his secretary. If he had had a private income he would be alive now. I looked at my in-laws cocooned in wealth and for a moment I hated them, as though my father's death was somehow their fault. I was completely out of control. My whole world seemed to have been ripped apart and as I sobbed loudly the gong summoned us to dinner. Erasmus did his best to calm me and suggested we should go straight over to my mother. For a moment Nora looked put out by this disruption of the Saturday routine.

'We can keep your dinner warm in the oven,' she said, and began to remove our place settings from the dining-room table.

My mother was brave. My sister too. I don't remember how Tam reacted but I am sure his behaviour was better than mine. I made rash promises to comfort my mother. We would rent part of her house. She need not be lonely or hard up. Promises made in a state of heightened emotion and destined not to be kept.

Next day, alone in the drawing-room with my father-in-law, I waited while he pushed his spectacles up his nose, cleared his throat and finally mustered enough courage to say what was worrying him,

'If there's any problem about the cost of the funeral, I would be very willing to pay.' How cruel kindness can be!

I sat through the funeral dry eyed, refusing to look at the coffin, concentrating my attention on a design for a new dress. Tightly fitting bodice, ashes to ashes, full skirt, dust to dust, buttons down the back, buttons covered with the same material which would have a dark background, black perhaps, yes black, black like my mother's widow weeds, and flowers, lots of flowers, so many wreaths, who had sent them and why had my aunts from Ireland brought lilies?

'Daddy hated the smell of lilies,' my sister whispered in my ear. It was all over. Now my regrets and self recriminations began.

I didn't really try to pull myself together. There was no point fighting such a tidal wave of misery. I stopped eating, lost weight, and cried for hours in bed at night. Dear, kind Theo suggested a treat in London and Nora readily agreed I should have the day off. We went to a café in Marylebone High Street where Theo, a connoisseur of cream cakes, knew they were the best in town. We behaved like schoolgirls playing truant, giggling at nothing and of course gossiping about the people safely out of earshot. I found the cream cakes disappointing but I got vicarious pleasure in watching Theo enjoy hers. When the waiter presented us with the bill I offered to pay my share but Theo protested that the tea had been her idea.

'What's it matter,' she said, 'It's all Barlow money anyway.'

Back at Boswells I began to mope again. Did Nora yearn for a cheerful evacuee to occupy my room?

'There's a small house near Hemel Hempstead which would suit you perfectly,' she said. With the particulars in her hand she looked really enthusiastic. That afternoon we drove over to inspect it. This was no make believe nonsense, this was the real thing, this charming house with its mellow, narrow Georgian bricks and honeysuckle round the door was going to be paid for by Nora, she made that clear. When we found that it was already bespoken I don't know which of us felt the most disappointed.

Horace's return from the long vac term coincided with a marked improvement in my spirits. Although he never mentioned the death of my father, he emanated sympathy and I benefited from his company until Nora announced that she had invited Clare Cornford to come and stay. The close affinity that cousins have excluded me.

They made wine together in the yard beneath my window and I could hear the fun they were having while I waited for Jeremy to perform on his pot. I felt old, weighed down by responsibilities and became such a wet blanket that Horace, my beloved brother-in-law, turned on me and said,

'You're getting on everyone's nerves – even Andrew's.' I had always been conscious of my own sensitive nerve endings, ready to be grated on by other peoples' behaviour, but now I allowed for the possibility that my dejected presence might be just as irritating to them. After a painful session of self-appraisal in the airing cupboard I decided to act as though I felt more cheerful, hoping that as the veneer grew thicker it would exert a kind of osmotic pressure and dilute my inner gloom. It worked, and in a perverse way the threat of invasion helped.

At any moment the church bells might ring the alarm that the Germans had landed. Sign posts disappeared and were dumped in back yards, their arms pointing up to heaven,

down into the earth, anywhere except in the right direction.
Names on stations were painted over and pill boxes, hastily
constructed, popped up in unlikely places. Nora looked at
one in the middle of a cornfield and said,

'One day we'll remember this time and think how they were
never used.' Her certainty that the Germans would not invade
this country convinced me, yet when we told each other our
dreams our repressed fears came out.

'The Germans came marching up the drive,' Nora said, 'led
by Ribbentrop and Goering.' She greeted them with her
usual politeness,

'Güten Tag, was wollen sie haben? The, oder Bier?' My
dream had the same beginning. The Germans came marching
up the drive but the refreshment I offered them was the sight
of me in a clean cotton dress holding my adorable baby in
my arms.

'That was enough to make them surrender,' I explained,
and Nora asked,

'Was it you or Jeremy who conquered them?'

10

Jeremy's first birthday, overshadowed by my father's death, had passed by with very little ceremony, apart from the garland of flowers which Nora made for him to wear round his head. 'A Darwin custom,' she explained. 'A charming one,' I replied.

While Jeremy opened his presents, Robert sat screaming on Theo's knee. He had to be held in a half nelson to stop him from grabbing the new toys. My Japanese, celluloid trash, found in a local shop, had more instant appeal but less life expectancy than Nora's solid wooden trolley bought from Galt's.

Offers to look after Jeremy diminished as his mobility increased. Now he could walk he was much more of a responsibility than that bundle lying in a pram. Susan, who had always been willing to keep an eye on him while he slept, could not be expected to follow him around the garden. Besides, with so many people staying in the house she had more than enough to do maintaining her high standards.

Nora had to shop for all those hungry mouths and cope with a fluctuating number of ration books. She was also becoming more involved with her own writing. The piles of papers that littered her bureau during the day disappeared under a piece of batik in the evening. None of us showed much respect for her work which we knew was vaguely connected with Charles Darwin.

When we received an invitation to a party in London I was ruthlessly determined to accept. Here was an opportunity to meet our friends, some of whom we hadn't seen for over a year. Nora must put Jeremy to bed that night. 'After all, he is her only grandchild,' I thought, and barged into the drawing-room where Nora sat at her desk. She looked dazed, as if in another world, and I couldn't understand the hesitation before she said 'yes'.

The journey to London was full of stops and starts which we

143

assumed was due to a faulty engine until on arriving at the station we saw a notice warning passengers of an alert. The ticket collector advised us to go back but we weren't willing to forgo our party as easily as that. We pushed our way through the crowds which seemed to be in a state of terrified flux, wanting to escape but not knowing where to go. A man holding a bloody handkerchief to his head completed the picture of panic. I felt no sense of fear, just a tingling excitement that here I was, in the centre of things, far away from the security of Boswells and the booming gong.

We walked quickly down Baker Street to the flat where the party was already under way. No need to find our hosts, I'm not even sure if they were there, and as for waiting to be introduced, that was unnecessary. Every time a bomb dropped the flat trembled and after a pause we all burst into laughter. We collected by the window, watching the sky grow more red, failing to connect that aggressive sunset with anyone being killed.

On our way back to the station an elderly man in a tin hat told us, between agitated blasts from his whistle, to take shelter. We went into a café called 'The Dutch Oven', where everything was in confusion and a waitress with such a shaky hand that she could hardly write down our order. We sat for hours in the train which refused to budge until the All Clear sounded. When we reached Wendover the glow in the sky was still there, visible thirty-six miles away. London was burning. Only now I thought of Tam. He who had 'left others to do the dirty work' was in the thick of it, risking his life to put out the flames and rescue bomb victims from the rubble.

We entered Boswells in the early hours of the morning. There was a note from Nora saying all had gone well and there was refreshment on the sideboard in the dining-room if we were hungry.

As the Battle of Britain progressed we became quite callous about the air raid warnings.

'Just another false alarm,' we would say, carrying on with what we were doing, assuming nothing would happen. One afternoon while we were having tea on the verandah, the All Clear sounded. We had not been aware of an alert and were laughing about this when someone shouted 'Look!' and pointed to the sky above the flowery valley. Two aeroplanes engaged in a dog fight were darting in and out of the clouds. We did not move from the table but sat there as though we were looking at a shot from an early thirties film. Nothing to worry about, the goodies always win. But did the goodies win? We never knew. The aeroplanes flew off into the distance and when they had finally disappeared from our sight, the siren got round to sounding the alert.

Londoners travelled out to Wendover to wrench a few hours undisturbed sleep from the countryside. Witchel Meadow, within easy reach of the station, was a popular resting place for weary individuals. A pin-stripe suit recumbent on the grass beside a bowler hat. . . .

Nora offered respite to the tired ambulance men in the East End. Those who were not daunted by the grandeur of dining in a big house enlivened the company which too often displayed that Pont cartoon 'a disinclination to sparkle'. The Cockney quick repartee and rhyming slang amused Nora, and she seemed to enjoy talking to the ambulance men more than she did to Geoffrey.

Erasmus had been studying every evening and most of the week-ends too for the Conjoint which he was due to sit at the end of October. Ben Burns, taking the same exam, drove over from Oxford. He didn't want to risk a disturbed night in London and asked for a bed in Boswells. All Nora could offer him was a Lilo on the schoolroom floor. Unfortunately the Lilo leaked and Ben spent much of the night on his hands and knees trying to fill it with air. However, he passed the exam. Erasmus did too. Susan was the first person to use the new handle to his name.

'If Doctor Barlow comes in late please remind him to lock the front door. Last night he must have forgotten because I found it open in the morning.' That 'Doctor Barlow' was like music to my ears and if she used it to deliver a reproof, what did I care?

Although I had encouraged Erasmus to work for his exam I often felt spurned when he did as I asked and left me alone while he got down to some serious cramming. The exam absorbing his attention became a person – another woman – who had come between us and was in danger of stealing his love. Resentment cropped up in many little ways and remarks intended to be loving turned into snide instead.

'So you're actually tearing yourself away from your work to be with me. . . .'

That was over now. My rival had disappeared and we were a loving couple again. Erasmus applied for a job – house physician at New End hospital. He was shortlisted. When he went for an interview I kissed him goodbye, not bothering to say 'Good Luck', so convinced was I of his success. There would be lots of other candidates, of course, but I was certain Erasmus would be the committee's choice. Geoffrey Keynes had built a great reputation at the New End hospital with his treatment for the thyroid and although I disapproved of nepotism, it could be accepted as a necessary evil, perhaps, in this case.

It was a frosty morning. Erasmus left on his motor bicycle, allowing ample time to get to London. Nora had also gone to town, catching an early train. I was making the beds when Susan tapped on the door.

'The group captain says you're wanted on the phone,' she said.

I ran down the back stairs to the study where Geoffrey sat at his desk in exactly the same position as he had been when I heard of my father's death. I felt no sense of déjà vu nor any premonition. After apologising to Geoffrey for disturbing his work, although he was only reading the newspaper, I took the telephone and said 'Hello'. There was no answering 'hello', just 'Dr Orme speaking.' Dr Orme had been our family's GP. I had known him all my life, why so curt? What was he saying? There had been an accident. Where? Two miles down the road. Who? Erasmus.

'I've got him here,' he said, 'I think you'd better come at once.'

I had no desire to freak out, to scream and hurl abuse as I had done when I heard of my father's death. I just clung to Geoffrey, saying,

'Take me to him, Geoffrey, please, please, take me to him now.'

I could hear my own voice pleading and see the shocked surprise in Geoffrey's eyes.

I plonked a protesting Jeremy in Susan's arms and without changing my bedroom slippers for outdoor shoes I jumped into Geoffrey's car. He was already in the front seat with the engine running.

On our way to Wendover I kept saying,

'If only his hands are all right.' Over and over again I said that, I don't know why. There was no possibility of Erasmus becoming a surgeon. Perhaps I was confusing him with Geoffrey, whose hands on the driving wheel looked sensitive and infinitely touchable.

When we drew up outside the house, Dr Orme immediately opened the front door. 'He's all right,' he said in that tone of voice which implies the exact opposite. He led us through the hall and into the surgery where Erasmus lay on a couch. His face was scarcely recognisable. After a quick examination of the gory mess Geoffrey reassured me.

'Only superficial cuts and grazes,' he said, 'they always look much worse than they really are.'

I took hold of Erasmus's hand and tried to warm it against my cheek. It was as cold as the ice that had caused the accident.

'I don't remember a thing,' he said, 'just my helmet full of blood.' Only a layer of fur lined leather to break the fall on the hard tarmac; there were no crash helmets in those days.

The blood came from his ear. I knew what that meant – a fractured skull. Tams' skull had been fractured when a drunk knocked him off his motor bicycle two miles down the road in the other direction. His ear had bled and bled. My mother nursed him at home. A bell rang when one of us had to fetch the doctor because his condition worsened. It all came back to me now.

What was Dr Orme saying? A bed in the local hospital. How could he suggest such an awful thing? I remembered him saying when I had measles,

'If she objects to being washed, send her to hospital, she won't be washed there.'

Erasmus must be tended by me. I was going to nurse him. Geoffrey agreed, I think he was the only one who did agree. Susan expressed her opinion in a loud voice outside my bedroom door.

'Doctor Erasmus would be much better off in hospital,' she told the cook. 'Mrs Erasmus should never ought to bring him here.'

Nora looked doubtful, too, but by then everything was fixed. She didn't say very much, she just helped me prepare

the room –a fire in the grate and hot bottles in the bed. I never
knew how she felt when the loudspeaker at Liverpool Street
Station called out her name and told her to go to the station-
master's office. But her reaction must have been the same as
mine would have been. She cancelled her visit to Cambridge
and returned at once to be with Erasmus. My husband,
her son.

When the ambulance arrived the two stretcher bearers
explained they weren't strong enough to carry Erasmus up the
stairs. One had a weak heart, the other a bad arm, and so it was
left to the women, Nora, Susan and me to get him into bed.
Every jolt hurt him, at every noise he cried out in pain. And of
course it had to be that afternoon that the winter supply of
coal was delivered into the yard beneath our bedroom. It
landed with an enormous crash and then the scrape, scrape,
crunch began as it was shovelled into bunkers. I protested
through the open window but the scraping of the metal on
concrete didn't stop. I needed Nora to exert her authority. She
had gone to the village to shop. Would Susan help? No. It was
not her job. Besides, if the garden boy didn't do it now, the
coal dust would spread all over the yard and people would
tramp dirt into the house.

'If Dr Erasmus wants peace and quiet,' she said, 'he should
have gone into hospital. . . .'

Geoffrey arranged for a neurologist from Halton camp hospital to see Erasmus. A handsome young man in uniform
stood at the end of the bed and diagnosed double vision by
holding up fingers for Erasmus to count. That would clear up
soon. Severe headaches might be the only complication. Of
course, he would have to take three months off work;
meanwhile, the only treatment was rest. That night I lay
beside Erasmus not daring to move in case I woke him up. He
was sleeping now and sleep was the best cure. I resented every
sound – the screech of an owl, the wind in the trees and that
distant rumble that grew louder and louder until it became a
terrible noise like furniture being moved in the sky.

'What the bloody hell is happening?' Erasmus moaned.

'Aeroplanes,' I replied, 'there must be hundreds of
them.'

'Well, I wish they'd go away.' They did. They went on their
way to bomb Coventry – the first of the cathedral cities to

suffer attack from the Luftwaffe.

I enjoyed my role of sick nurse very much. It made a pleasant change to have Erasmus tied to one spot, needing me, while I was the one who went in and out of the door with reassuring remarks that I wouldn't be away for long. Nora complimented me on what she called 'rising wonderfully to the occasion', but she couldn't resign herself to my performing one of the more basic tasks.

'A wife shouldn't have to empty a bed pan,' she said, and went into action to relieve me of a duty which I didn't mind in the very least. An agency provided a nurse, or rather an exquisite tussore silk uniform who could arrange flowers, set trays and nothing much else. The useless creature, failed tart, ex-model, committed three serious crimes in Nora's eyes which would be listed in her dossier as:

No ration book.

Butter left on edge of plate.

Excess sugar found in tea cup.

After she went, flowers drooped in their vases, tray cloths disappeared and we all sighed with relief.

Erasmus was now convalescent. Very convalescent.

'I've nothing to do but pick the scabs off my face,' he complained. He was still forbidden to look at print but that didn't prevent his eyes from following me around the room.

'What a lot of time you spend looking in the mirror,' he said, 'I'd no idea you were so vain.' The beast. The ungrateful beast. Here was I slaving away for his comfort, working my fingers to the bone on his behalf, and he dared to criticise me. Of course I had to glance in the mirror, how else could I be sure I looked all right? I went in search of Nora to tell her exactly what I thought of her horrible son.

She was in the drawing-room, sitting at a small table, working on the papers which had overflowed from her bureau. Her back, stiff with concentration, was towards me, yet when she turned round there was no irritation on her face. She smiled and I was suddenly conscious of the patience behind that smile. I had done a lot of patient smiling myself in the last few weeks.

'Erasmus has been doing a time and motion study on me,' I complained. It sounded a very lame excuse for interrupting her.

'I'm sorry,' I said, 'I'm disturbing your work. I'm so sorry, I really shouldn't have done that.'

She gave a wistful glance across the flowery valley and said, very slowly, as though the suggestion she was making was forming in her mind as she spoke,

'There's a cottage belonging to a friend of mine at Hotley Bottom. It will be vacant over Christmas, why don't the three of you go there for a break?' Perhaps she needed the break from us? That thought occurred to me for the first time.

Our brief stay in the cottage was fun. Everything we did there was fun. Fetching water down the road from the pump was fun. Eating meals, cooked on an ancient kitchen range was fun, delicious fun, especially when every mouthful compared very favourably to anything we had tasted at Boswells. Even washing-up in the scullery was fun; the frequent air-raid warnings turned it into a game, a kind of Tom Tidler's ground, with a quick nip to the lean-to scullery at the back as soon as the All Clear sounded. By the light of a torch propped against a tap the washing-up had to be done as quickly as possible before the alert sounded again. Nappies grew greyer each day, but that was all part of the primitive fun, which did not prevent us from enjoying a hot bath when we returned to civilization again.

We did not stay at Boswells very long. There was just time for Erasmus to apply for a job at UCH before we were off to Oxford. He was going to ease himself into working by doing some research for Zolly Zuckerman. We shared a flat with a friend in a house which later became a pub, The Black Horse. It was a makeshift arrangement which suited me well. We all mucked in together. There was always someone from another flat to be with Jeremy if we wanted to go out, a reciprocal arrangement that never went sour. The communal kitchen in the basement had several gas stoves and a huge table. The people who collected there to prepare dinners were mostly academics, a far cry from those debutantes who used to sabotage my cooking.

Aunt Helen, as generous with her friends' hospitality as she was with her own, told us to contact Ruth Spooner, a spinster of similar calibre as herself. We were invited out to dinner in a house along the Banbury Road. Nora had made me very cons-cious of ration book entertaining and it was a great treat to be served a macaroni pie which was a guilt-free gastronomic delight. Ruth Spooner belonged to the generation when talk in any size, large or small, was a natural accompaniment to eating, and conversation flowed until Erasmus suddenly turned deathly pale, dropped his knife and fork and put his head in his hands.

This was the first of the devastating headaches that incapaci-tated him from time to time. They descended without rhyme or reason and although we searched for an explanation, physical or psychological, none was ever found.

After our short spell of independence in Oxford we returned to Boswells. An important milestone would soon be reached. Erasmus had got the job of house physician to Harold Himsworth and was to take up residence at UCH on March the first. My pleasure in his getting such an excellent post began to diminish as the time for separation approached. A six month residential house job was part of his medical qualification. It came as no surprise. I had planned for this as soon as I became pregnant with Jeremy. I would go 'home', and become a daughter again, adored by my father and encouraged to be a better person by my mother. Everyone would dote on the baby and I would create a nursery in one of the rooms with pretty wallpaper, teddy bears and trains, with frilly curtains fluttering in the breeze and stretches of lino which was always very clean. Dreams, dreams, dreams. . . .

On a cold raw morning without the faintest hint of spring Nora drove me and Jeremy over to Prestwood where my mother had moved into a smaller house. A house which was too small for the furniture but not small enough to save work. My mother made a brave attempt at that hospitable welcome which had been such a feature of my childhood. She led us into the sitting-room where the familiar square dining-room table which had before seemed quite a reasonable size now occupied most of the floor. There was no fire in the grate.

'The coal ration must be kept for Tam,' she explained, 'he comes home exhausted. He's having a terrible time, air raids every night. I don't know how he stands it.' I felt we were intruders and resented it.

Nora clearly hated leaving us here. Knowing how much

more Boswells had to offer in space alone, she must have wondered what we were doing unloading the suitcases and bulging carrier bags into the chilly hall. I went out to the car to say goodbye. She did not try to conceal her anxiety.

'You will come back for Erasmus's week-ends off, won't you?' she asked. One week-end a month. My lip trembled, I nodded my head, not daring to speak and was surprised to see tears in Nora's eyes, too.

It took less than two weeks for my mother to reach the end of her taut tether. A credit to her patience that she managed to contain her indignation that long. I moved in with my mother for a six months' long stay expecting some sort of special treatment to compensate for my separation from Erasmus, without appreciating that everyone had troubles enough of their own. My mother, brave as she was, hadn't yet adapted to being a widow. Tam was beginning to crack from the strain of the raids in the East End. Gill, saddened by a broken engagement, was not her usual sanguine self and Teedie, an occasional visitor-without-ration-book had sufficient matrimonial difficulties to keep him permanently on edge.

We had suddenly become an unhappy family, with each of us unhappy in our own way.

Just as a relatively trivial issue of an Archduke's murder led to the Great War, nappies airing in front of the fire caused my mother finally to lose control and explode.

Lectures about misbehaviour of some sort or another had punctuated my adolescence but what happened now amounted to complete character annihilation. It began with my total lack of consideration for Tam. He came home expecting to relax comfortably – how could he with a towel horse in front of the fire, and the room filled with a smell of drying nappies? I had spoilt his brief leave. That led all in one breath to the more basic fault of egocentricity. I only thought about myself and my own problems which, compared to other people's problems, weren't really problems at all. She had heard my hysterical sobbing at night, keeping everyone awake, bemoaning the fact that I would not be with Erasmus for a whole month. How fortunate I was to have such a brief separation while others. . . . She didn't have to spell out her own suffering. I knew what she meant. My mother had a great gift with words. She could have been addressing a whole audience instead of me lying on the unmade bed, crimson in the face from the verbal onslaught.

My immediate reaction after this row, the grand finale, the last row I ever had with my mother, was to pack and go. But where? Back to Boswells? No. I couldn't bring myself to do that, an explanation would have to be given, unless I told some corking lie which might easily end up by adding coals of fire to my head. I advertised in the *New Statesman*.

'Mother with well-behaved two year old willing to do domestic work in return for accommodation.' I received one dubious reply with nasty insinuations from a farmer in Sussex and another from Horace. He had seen the advertisement and although I had only given a box number he guessed it had come from me.

Horace had often been my confidant. From those early days at West Runton we had always been able to communicate. He could pick up a nuance quicker than anyone I knew. After a brief conversation on the phone he recognised my 'situation required' advertisement for what it was and offered a short term solution. Would I, he asked, come with him to work at a rest centre in the East End of London? Air raids were bad, the voluntary services desperate for help, our country needed us and I was keen to get away from home.

Nora, impressed by this apparent awakening of my social conscience, readily agreed to look after Jeremy for the week I would be away. A mother was not so easily taken in, but she stopped the cynical shakes of her head when I told her we were going to be housed in a school off the Commercial Road.

'You'll be near Tam,' she said, 'you'll visit him at the fire station, won't you?'

'Of course. Of course. That will be the first thing I'll do.'

We parted on good terms. She waved me goodbye from the door. I marched off down the hill to the station humming 'It's a long way to Tipperary.'

Only when I reached the rest centre, a gaunt building built between the wars, did Horace bother to tell me that Clare Cornford was also coming to help. She and I joked about who was chaperoning whom and behind the joke there was a grain of truth, perhaps?

Crammed into a small classroom was a mountain of clothes from America. Every day we sorted them into bundles. A yellow tee shirt with 'Confucius he said' written in black letters across it struck us as tremendously funny; we had never seen a tee shirt with a slogan before.

When Clare worked on a different shift Horace and I explored the back streets leading down to the Thames, picking our way through the debris of burnt-out warehouses, admiring the architecture of Georgian squares, climbing through fences to find rural quiet on a tow-path beside a canal, and of course visiting the fire station. Tam, in uniform, demonstrated the speedy descent down the greasy pole and introduced us to his friends.

In the evening we prepared for action, and sure enough, as soon as it was dark, the siren wailed and the bombing began. Bang, crash, wallop; the noise became deafening with the bustling agitation as people jostled each other to get through the door into the school hall. We served them cocoa; endless mugs of steaming cocoa we handed round with the bright smiles and cheery words that cut no ice with the resigned East Enders who knew we were probably more frightened than they were.

We snatched sleep when we could in a communal dormitory up several flights of stairs. We pushed our beds together and held hands in the dark.

Bombs or anti-aircraft barrage? It was difficult to tell which was which, but when there was a crash and the whole building shook as if in fear, we knew a bomb had landed very near. Until that moment I felt exhilaration rather than fear, but from now on I began to question why I was there. What would happen if that bomb had hit the school rather than the houses in the next street?

Why had I agreed to risk my life like this when my real responsibility lay with looking after my own child? By the end of the week I was thankful to return home. We travelled through the city on the top deck of a bus, united by exhaustion, unable to comment on the devastation we saw.

I now knew what Tam was suffering in the East End. I tried to temper my mother's concern with banal comments about the wonderfully brave job he was doing for his country.

'I don't care about the country, I only care about him,' she replied tartly. We were both thankful when Tam, after saving a man from a blazing building, was sent home on sick leave. He was awarded a medal for his brave rescue. We didn't know that then; he was just a haggard, jittery ghost whom the doctor said must rest. I took him up his breakfast in bed. Every morning I cooked him eggs and bacon with slabs of fried bread. My mother's breakfast, a more frugal affair, I carried up on a tray to her room, and Jeremy, soon after he awoke, was tucked under Tam's eiderdown and fed with crusts of toast until his porridge was ready downstairs. I drank my coffee on the run while tidying the house. The stairs became my obsession. They always had to be brushed and dusted before I took Jeremy out.

That morning walk never varied. Down the 'unadopted' road with holes of water as brown as strong tea, up to the corner where the village idiot stood gesticulating, back along the pavement with the excitement of cars and lorries, and after a quick visit to the shops return home. When I had settled Jeremy in his playpen it was time to prepare lunch.

Every day was the same but the boring routine had rewards. Tam was recovering and becoming the brother I had always known. We slipped into our earlier relationship. Although we didn't have fights with greengage jam as we did when we were young we laughed a lot and generated jollity, which my mother liked. I was no longer in her bad books. Perhaps she thought the row had done me good. Maybe she was right?

When Erasmus had his weekends off he went to Boswells. I always expected too much from these brief reunions and invariably ended up feeling crabby and disappointed. There wasn't enough time to throw off the lives we had left behind and the fact that our wants conflicted made matters worse. Erasmus, having been on call day and night at the hospital, needed sleep and to be soothed. I craved for entertainment. During Jeremy's afternoon sleep we tried the panacea for all ills, indoors and *al fresco*, but either Susan started her hymn singing outside our bedroom door or heavy footsteps disturbed us in the long grass.

I tried the other panacea and bought myself a new dress with a very full, flared skirt that needed shortening. Nora supplied the scissors and round and round I went, snipping away at the hem until there was practically no skirt left. That dress was the last of a dying breed before clothes rationing began. Fashions became austere to save material and always bore the CC41 tag until after the war was over and the New Look appeared.

'You won't like this latest restriction,' Nora said to me, knowing how much pleasure I got from clothes. Food rationing was a tiresome inconvenience not to be compared with the rationing of clothes which struck at the core of my vanity.

'What coupons are we to use?' I asked in a panic. No-one seemed to know until an official from the Board of Trade announced 'The margarine coupons in the ration book can be exchanged for clothes.' A strange piece of Civil Service logic.

On one of these frustrating week-ends Nora found me sitting alone on the verandah, feeling and no doubt looking, very disgruntled.

'How about helping me string some beans?' she asked. I submitted to the therapy. As we sat together in the sunshine with our hands occupied she began talking about Alan, which was her oblique way of empathising with me.

'At first he only spent a night or two at the Savile. Now it's most of the week and I'm lucky if he comes down on Friday night. We only have time to discuss plans. Sometimes I really think he prefers his club to his home.'

'And what's he doing at his club?' I asked, genuinely curious. Any other wife would have sighed, but Nora never indulged in self-pity.

'Playing bridge. Drinking. Going to the shelter when there's a raid.' Her matter of fact tone brightened:

'We've had some wonderful holidays together. Climbing in the Alps and collecting wild flowers. That was when the children were young. I hated leaving them of course but the further I went the less I cared.' She began to laugh. 'It was as though I was throwing one child out of the window for every mile we went in the train.'

Oddly enough, we managed to recapture the honeymoon atmosphere during Erasmus's MB examination. Four whole nights together in a blissfully comfortable double bed while we stayed with Gwen Raverat at Harlton, near Cambridge.

The weather was idyllic. When Erasmus wasn't sweating over his papers indoors we took Jeremy on the motorbicycle, wedging him between us, as we drove along straight roads between cornfields in the flat countryside, none of us wearing crash helmets, of course.

Gwen showed great forebearance in not criticising what we did. She never hinted that perhaps Erasmus's time could be better spent in revising or that it wasn't safe for Jeremy and me to ride on the pillion of a motorbicycle which had already been the cause of one major accident.

Jeremy's demand to have his pudding before his first course she accepted without questioning the rights and wrong of giving in to such an unorthodox request.

'He's a most sensible child,' she insisted. 'Look at him now playing with those bowls. Julian Trevelyan would throw them all into the long grass but Jeremy just rolls them along the lawn.' I was delighted this should be Jeremy's reputation, knowing what weight Gwen's opinions carried with the family.

I fell in love with Harlton. The garden, the house and Gwen herself had been given just the right amount of care. Gwen worked very hard, getting up early and going off to Cambridge to spend hours doing meticulous drawings for an Admiralty project, yet she still found time for her art, and for sitting in the garden talking to me. I admired her. I thought we were getting on very well until I offered to help with the dinner and she suggested I made a stew. What could be easier, I thought, and rolled up my sleeves, ready to get on with the job. Carrots, potatoes, onions were predictably placed in a strange kitchen, but where was the Oxo cube? I opened drawers, searched cupboards. No Oxo cube. I would ask Gwen. That was a terrible *faux pas*. Gwen had spent years in France. A stew for her was garlic, wine and bay leaves. She had to be reminded what an Oxo cube was, and then – whoosh! came the disapproval.

She could hardly bring herself to say the word   Oxo cube. Nothing so low, so utterly English and working class, had ever found its way into her house, her kitchen or her stew!

Erasmus's exams seemed fated to be dogged by historical events. Last time it was the fall of France, this year Germany invaded Russia. When I met Erasmus after his exam, in the

Corn Exchange, he didn't want to discuss his papers; all he cared about was Hitler's latest move.

'Fighting on two fronts, that's exactly what Hitler swore he'd never do.'

'Hitler's mad,' was my only comment.

I couldn't share Erasmus's delight that the Communists were now our allies. I had something more important on my mind.

'If you pass your exam I'm going to have another baby,' I said.

The following week I went to London on a very special mission. Erasmus met me in the main hall of the hospital wearing his white coat and greeting me as though I were his patient. A professional smile was all I got – a kiss would have been against medical etiquette. He escorted me up the wide staircase, along a corridor and into the residents' quarters. Now his manner changed; holding me by the hand he led me quickly down a passage to a room at the end. This was where he slept. The room was no bigger than a cell but it had all we needed – a chair, which propped under the handle of the door would ensure we were not disturbed, and a bed.

I spent the rest of the day wandering round the baby department of a big store. Should I buy a matinee jacket in pink or blue? It must be a girl. Another boy would mean I had half the number of sons in the Keynes family. Those little horrors who shouted 'Widdershins' when I passed the port the wrong way round made me dread a family of boys. I looked at frilly pants and petticoats and finally sacrificed some of my maragarine coupons for a dress with rosebuds embroidered on it. I went home with a smile on my face. The smile stayed until my period came on.

My mother could hear me venting my disappointment on the stair carpet outside her room. 'What's the matter?' she called out. I told her what had happened and she was lavishly sympathetic. Tam had to get up for breakfast next morning and I was the one who had a tray carried up to me in bed. Extra pillows were put behind my head and I was encouraged to stay where I was by being given the *New Statesman* to read. Usually I began at the back, limbering up with the advertisements before working my way through to the heavier stuff at the front, but today I stuck at one advertisement which made me laugh.

'Domestic misfit requires summer job. Prepared to do absolutely anything,' it said. Tam and I concocted an answer.

'Dear Domestic Misfit, if you are prepared to empty chamber pots, wash nappies, peel potatoes and work from dawn to midnight, please come.'

To our surprise we received by return a serious reply and before we could put the plan into reverse a young man was occupying the spare room. He looked like Oscar Wilde, modelled himself on Oscar Wilde and talked endlessly about his homosexual tendencies, which went hetero when we washed up the supper alone in the kitchen.

The only other thing our domestic misfit did, apart from falling in love with me every evening, was to fillet herrings. The Ministry of Food recipes which appeared in the newspapers told us how this cheap, nourishing fish could be fried, baked, coated with oatmeal, stuffed with parsley, soused in vinegar and eaten every day. And that's exactly what we did until Erasmus arrived to take me and Jeremy away on the motorbike. Boswells again.

The six month separation was over and a less trying one about to begin. Erasmus accepted a job in Lewisham which was only partly residential. Every week-end would be free and only a few nights each week would have to be spent in the hospital. I now felt justified in making a home. Geoffrey suggested we should move into his house in Arkwright Road which was empty apart from a housekeeper, her husband and her little boy living in the basement.

'Mrs Tanner is a marvellous cook,' he said, 'She's an absolute dear and I know she would love to have you there.' We believed him. If Nora had her doubts, and I can't believe she hadn't, she kept them to herself.

I was pregnant when we moved into the big ugly house which, with its flashes of white paint on dark bricks, resembled a mouthful of dental decay. Mrs Tanner, a pale, delicate woman, appeared exhausted before we got inside the door. 'Sandwalk', where Geoffrey and Margaret normally slept, was allocated to us, with Jeremy sleeping in Geoffrey's dressing-room next door. Downstairs the dining-room, leading out onto a terrace and the large garden, was at our disposal. Everything had been done for our comfort. Margaret had left out toys for Jeremy, toys she had played with as a child. Bricks which made a charming old-fashioned picture when arranged the right way in their box. I liked the surrealist effect of boots sticking out of ringlets and an apron changing place with a dimpled face. Heirlooms which had survived the Keynes children showed signs of disintegrating with me in charge. Somehow it invariably rained if toys were left out on the terrace. I have shaming memories of those pictures coming adrift from the precious bricks.

I felt ghastly. Morning sickness, if it had been true to its name, would be bearable, but my morning sickness lasted the whole twenty-four hours. Mrs Tanner fulfilled Geoffrey's promise of being an excellent cook, but unfortunately I could hardly bring myself to eat any of the dishes she prepared. I longed to go to bed and stay there for the duration but Jeremy had to have his daily walk; Truby King still ruled, even when I felt as I did. Down by the Leg of Mutton pond the seagulls squawked and soared overhead while we threw our crusts of bread at the ducks. One day a little boy appeared at our side to watch. A future friend for Jeremy, I hoped, and immediately engaged the mother in conversation.

'He's going to the country tomorrow,' she said, 'no self-respecting child is in London these days.'

Margaret Keynes came up to see how we were getting on. She was horrified by the downstairs lavatory where torn up pieces of newpaper lay strewn over the floor. Toilet rolls were in very short supply and I didn't feel well enough to trail around the shops looking for them. Also a vital part of a wooden train was missing, but worst of all was Jeremy's shaven head, which called for an explanation I was loath to give.

The discovery of lice coincided with our arrival in Arkwright Road. Not just one or two lice but generations prowled around in the jungle of thick hair. A doctor recommended lotion and special soap, but the lice continued to multiply until Erasmus, in desperation, decided to cut them off at source and shaved the hair from Jeremy's head. And all this in Geoffrey's most intimate domain; his dressing-room and bathroom, which normally bore his stamp with tortoiseshell brushes and cut-glass bottles, now was sullied by our fine tooth combs and pungent lotions.

We were like the worst kind of evacuees arriving with an infested head. My excuses sounded terribly lame; he must have caught nits from a child in the playground or coming up in the train or. . . . In the glare of Margaret's charitable smile my imagination ran dry. We lapsed into silence, scratching our heads, until Margaret announced it was time to go. But the front door didn't bang from her departure for another quarter of an hour, not until she had had a heart to heart with Mrs Tanner. The outcome of that conversation became clear when Geoffrey arrived the following day.

His unexpected visit found the sitting-room scattered with toys, and a chair, *his* chair, had to be cleared of Dinky cars before he could sit down. He smiled and smiled and tried to maintain his suave image, but feet kept ruffling the hearth rug and only after it had been straightened several times could he come to the point. Mrs Tanner found us too much work. She wasn't strong. Jeremy and myself and Erasmus's twice weekly visits had already taken a toll of her health. We must go. Yes, go. The room reeked of embarrassment. I wanted to open the window to let in fresh air. He said he was sorry. I said I was sorry. Of course we must go, but where?

Mercifully there were more relations in the pipeline prepared to offer us a roof over our heads. The Darwins, Bernard and his wife Eily, had vacated their house in Kent after a bomb landed in the field next to them. They offered us a six month's lease at thirty shillings a week; a low rent because we would be doing them a service by living there. Without us in occupation a big house like Gorringes might be commandeered by the airforce, based at Biggin Hill, not far from Downe.

We left Arkwright Road in a taxi. Jeremy's excitement at this novel form of transport took the edge off Mrs Tanner's tearful goodbye. She stood on the pavement waving a damp handkerchief. She really seemed to mind our leaving although she could not have borne it if we had stayed.

There had been no time to inspect our latest home. We accepted the Darwin's kind offer blindfold because Downe was in easy reach of Lewisham and what mattered most was an uncomplicated journey for Erasmus on his motor bicycle.

I knew Gorringes was close to the sacred ground where Charles Darwin had lived. Every day the great man took a walk through the trees along the sandwalk (scratching his head?) and pondered on his theories of evolution. I imagined that Erasmus's connection with the village would ensure us a warm welcome. The first hint that this might not be so came on our arrival when I called on the gardener to collect the key of the house. . . . He was surly, and his wife, who lurked behind him, had a hostile stare. We could be spies, dropped by enemy aircraft, or worse still, poor relations who couldn't afford a decent pram and would not be generous with a Christmas tip.

'I come in twice daily to stoke the boiler,' the gardener said, making it sound like a threat rather than a useful service.

'That heats the water?' I asked.

'Should do,' he replied, and his wife added, 'until the anthracite runs out.'

I longed to be given a cup of tea and allowed to sit down in front of a warm fire.

'And the shops?' I continued the conversation hoping they would take pity on us, but the wife had already started to close the door.

'There's a grocery store and a butcher which Mrs Darwin always used, but then of course she had a car.'

Eily had written that the gardener's wife always helped with the cleaning of the house and would be delighted, she was sure, to do the same for me. Wary now of kind offers, I phrased my request in general terms. Before the door finally closed in my face I was told that Mrs Daniels in the big house at the end of the village employed all the available help.

Gorringes was a long, low house, undeniably Regency in spite of the muddly bits which had been added here and there. Eily, in one of her vague, rambling letters, had suggested we would be most comfortable in the nursery wing which had two communicating bedrooms at the back, overlooking an unkempt garden dominated by a huge cedar. Our sitting-room, the original nursery, had a long window running almost the entire length of the wall with a window seat which I immediately slumped down on, thinking,

'This is nice, this is where I shall sit and watch the seasons come and go.' Autumn has already touched the leaves on the avenue of trees which led to the village.

Unrealistically I imagined that because I was in a big house there would be a staff of servants to do the work, but there was no-one, absolutely no-one, tucked away in any of the musty, shuttered rooms. I tried to pretend it was all very exciting even though it would soon be dark and I had yet to discover the layout of the scullery and unblock the sink.

When the door bell rang I ran to answer it, thankful that my sister, Gill, who had promised to spend the first few nights with me had come earlier than expected. She would find the saucepans in the kitchen; she wouldn't mind going into the garden to check the black-out; she would sit and talk with me in front of the gas fire and tell me not to be silly when I jumped at strange noises. But my sister wasn't on the doorstep; a boy with a telegram stood there instead. Gill was ill.

'Any reply?' he asked. I shook my head. 'Not bad news, I hope,' he said and quickly rode off on his bicycle. My last link with the outside world had gone.

The house grew larger at night. It was large enough during the day but in the dark it assumed gigantic proportions. Doors banged. Wainscotting creaked. Out in the garden trees whispered conspiratorily while the huge cedar waved its arms and shook its head as if to say my coming here was a dreadful mistake. In bed I couldn't sleep. I lay rigid waiting for the siren to scream, waiting for Jeremy to scream, wanting to scream myself, unable to relax until the curtains became a shade lighter and the house shrank back to its normal size.

I enquired at the grocery store and at the butchers about living-in help, a lodger, a companion, I didn't mind who or what provided another human being was in the house at night. The answer was no, the same looking-down-the-nose response that I always got when I asked for any favour, a tin of prunes off points or unrationed offal. However, the word went round that I had a spare room and a soldier's wife turned up with a fat, white slug of a baby called Kevin. She slept in the grander part of the house, sharing a bed with her son. She didn't seem very keen to do much work. When her husband came home for a brief leave I never saw her at all. She spent the entire forty-eight hours with him and the baby in the bedroom.

After her husband had gone she started polishing the hall floor, pushing the hefty, old-fashioned dubber to and fro with an energy that impressed me until I discovered it was just a means to an end – her period was late and she hoped violent exercise might bring it on. One child was quite enough, she said, although I couldn't see that Kevin was any trouble. Bottle fed, and not allowed a breath of fresh air, he broke all the Truby King rules by thriving, never crying or getting ill.

When Mrs Daniels called I was proud to invite her into the gleaming hall. She brought with her an invitation to tea which I assumed included Jeremy and was not for me alone. Her surprise when the two of us arrived made me realise I had committed a social blunder. Tea was laid out on a small table in front of a blazing fire and had to be re-arranged to accommodate a two year old whose whims, which seemed reasonable enough at home, now appeared to be the ravings of a lunatic. And a jar of honey didn't help. While arguing about how and where the honey should be spread on flimsy triangles of brown bread I tried to carry on a rational conversation with my hostess who in one long patriotic breath described how by keeping bees, chickens and a domestic staff she contributed to the war effort.

'Have you enough help?' She asked. I described the soldier's wife and admitted I never knew exactly what she did, apart from getting pregnant and polishing the hall. That failed to get a laugh.

'Cynthia has a nanny,' I was told. I had no idea who Cynthia was. 'Such a nice gal from Yorkshire. She'd be lawst without her because she works full-time with the Red Craws.'

And you'll be very craws, I thought, if any more dollops of honey fall on the carpet. A maid coming into the room to draw the heavy brocade curtains gave me an excuse to leave before it got too dark.

'You haven't a car?'

'No. My husband has a motor-bike.'

'Oh . . . well . . . goodbye. . . .' She rang for the parlour-maid to see us out. At any rate she didn't commit perjury by saying she would like to see us again, I thought, the most charitable thought I had that afternoon.

Nora came to stay, bringing with her a jar of delicious marmalade made from many different ingredients; apples, carrots, dates, but no oranges. They had disappeared from the shops.

She took me to Downe House. Although not usually given to living in the past she suddenly began to reminisce about the happy times she had had there as a child.

'We were always sent with our nurse,' she said, 'whom we loved very much. She made sure we were comfortable – as long as she was there we knew everything would be all right.' We walked quickly through Charles Darwin's study without pausing to genuflect at his desk, and the family bible – *The Origin of Species* – only received a cursory glance. Nora was intent on finding the back stairs that led to the nursery.

'We played games in this room with our cousins,' she said. 'They were our closest friends, we didn't bother with anyone else. There was no need. Frances and Gwen were such stimulating companions – and Margaret, of course.' She looked around the room as if expecting to see them there and then said,

'I think I really preferred our nurse to my mother. I liked the feel of her rough, capable hands. It was awful when my mother put me to bed.'

We walked round the garden. Nora disapproved of some of the changes that had been made; anything that was unnaturally lush, she dismissed as vulgar. The gardener looked nipped after her frosty response to his gaudy chrysanthemums in the greenhouse.

On our way home I told her about the disastrous tea party at Mrs Daniels. She didn't quite appreciate the humour of my account, it was as though she took Mrs Daniels' side. I suddenly needed her to see it from my point of view. I added the bit about Mrs Daniels' non-reaction to the soldier's wife getting pregnant and polishing the hall.

'I expect you told her that to shock rather than amuse,' Nora said, and after a pause added, 'Did you wear those shoes when you went out to tea?'

I was about to say 'Yes, and why not?' when I noticed the uppers. They were coming apart from the sole and one of the broken laces had been clumsily knotted. I was shabby. I had failed to heed the woman's magazine warning. I had let myself go.

When Nicola Darwin came to stay she saw the shrunken yellowed vests and much washed knickers hanging on the line. She suggested, in the nicest possible way, which can be doubly hurtful but wasn't in this case, buying me some more when she went back to London. Joan's visit produced positive results. She ferretted out everything that needed mending and then set to with the same dedication with which she had repaired things at Boswells. Jeremy's sleeping bag, which looked like a saint's relic, more suitable for a glass case in a cathedral than nightwear for a little boy, received maximum attention.

December. The Japanese bombed Pearl Harbour, the Americans came into the war and I started preparing for Christmas. The Ministry of Food told me to take one carrot, chop it, grate it, boil it, fry it, do what I liked with it but for God's sake eat it. There was a carrot mountain and every recipe contained at least one carrot. We, the gullible public, were told that carrots helped us to see in the dark. Then of course there was the ubiquitous dried egg, which, mixed with water, looked like a baby's motion and smelled much worse.

As the season of good will approached, the shop-keepers became increasingly morose. Tins of beetroot supplanted tins of rhubarb and things which had been scarce disappeared altogether from the shelves. I decided to try my luck by travelling further afield, to Orpington, where there was a market on Wednesdays. In order to get there, complicated arrangements had to be made: Jeremy bribed with the promise of a present to stay with Kevin, whom he disliked. The soldier's wife bribed with a couple of pound notes to keep an eye on Jeremy, whom she disliked because he was interfering with her afternoon rest. And I disliked hanging around for the bus which arrived twenty minutes after the timetable said it would and 'didn't I know there was a war on?' when I complained it was late.

The cross-country journey provided an interesting tour of small villages, but by the time I reached Orpington and had found my way to the market, many of the stalls were already closing down. I wandered around, decidely peeved, until I saw a bloody, literally bloody, rabbit hanging on a wire from an awning. Beneath that fur was coupon-free, solid protein – my luck was in at last. The man who sold it explained he was eager to get home and he gave me his last remaining carrier bag as a gesture of good will. After wishing me a happy Christmas he said:

'You'll enjoy that.' I smiled, nodded and agreed that I would.

Back on the bus I remembered Mrs Tanner's excellent rabbit pie. My crust would be better than hers because I would make rough puff pastry from my carefully hoarded margarine and lard. What a wonderful surprise for Erasmus on Christmas eve! I glowed with a sense of future achievement until a smell very much in the present which I had been trying to ignore became so pungent that I wondered if I had dog's mess on my shoes. No, they were perfectly clean. Could the smell be coming from the soldier sitting behing me? Yes, I was sure it was his sweaty feet; but when he got off the bus the smell didn't go with him. It remained and if anything, got worse. I opened the carrier bag and a noxious stench escaped. The bloody rabbit! No wonder it had been hanging there all alone.

My wonderful Christmas eve surprise ended up in a ditch, enjoyed by rats or a stray dog, I hope. As things turned out, even if it had been cooked to perfection with *fresh*, tender meat falling off the bones beneath a high rise pastry crust we would never have been able to enjoy it because Jeremy, after tea, in a state of pre-Christmas excitement, tripped on the hearth rug and fell backwards into the gas fire. I pulled him out before his clothes caught alight but his thighs had already made contact with the red hot fender's metal lining. They were badly burnt. A chaotic Christmas eve merged into a distraught Christmas day. We hovered over his cot where he lay, his legs covered in gentian violet. He was too ill to unwrap any of his presents.

Why wasn't there a guard in front of the fire? Because there wasn't a guard to put there. We tried to buy one in Lewisham and Orpington but the answer was always the same – they had just sold the last one and were waiting for the next supply. What about the Army and Navy Stores? They would be sure to have one, especially for a customer with an account there. We haven't got an account at the Army and Navy stores. No account at the Army and Navy stores, why ever not? We're too broke, there wouldn't be any point. Too bloody broke.

Was Alan's letter, written on Savile club notepaper, a direct result of this cross-examination in which our only hope was to claim mitigating circumstances? I shall never know. It was addressed to us both; from the wobbly hand that slanted across the page he could have written it late at night when very tired or slightly drunk. After initial conventional wishes for the new year he came to the point and suggested a budget that would enable us to live within the income that Erasmus now earned. A top civil servant in the Treasury, no doubt, could give excellent advice on running the finances of the country, but when it came to running a household he seemed out of touch, inept. However, I took the advice in the spirit in which I hoped it was given, a genuine desire to help although impossible to follow. The clothing allowance for us all was fifteen pounds a year without any concessions to the expected baby. Had we tried to live within the suggested amount for heating, we would have died of hypothermia, I am sure.

It became cold. Very cold indeed. General Winter, whom Hitler feared more than any other general, swept across Europe and entered Britain, freezing the ground solid, the ponds solid and the pipes solid. Erasmus could not go to work until he had poured a kettle of boiling water over the tank of the motorbike. Even the petrol had frozen.

After a dramatic blizzard which for a brief while turned the garden into a dazzling, magical white, the clouds gathered solid. Only an occasional flurry of small flakes dropped out of the grey, constipated sky, which needed a purge before the sun would shine again.

Snowmen, all shapes and sizes, stood still on what had once been a lawn, while clothes indoors scorched in front of the fire. The preparation time for going out took longer than the time spent in the biting cold air. The white sound of the frozen world made me hate the snow.

January, February, March – always the same view from the long sitting-room window, until suddenly the weather changed. Almost overnight the avenue of trees blurred with bursting buds, birds sang more loudly than they had ever sung before, and bulbs splashed colour everywhere. Spring arrived and the Darwins arrived too.

Owing to some change in their plans the tenants and the landlords overlapped for a week. What should have been a recipe for disaster turned out to be a great success. Instead of finding fault with everything, the Darwins were delighted with the state of the house. Perhaps the hall, thanks to the soldier's wife, created such an impression when they came through the front door that they were blinded to anything else.

'It's never looked like that before. I can see the parquet pattern round the edge now,' exclaimed Eily.

Neighbours appeared from nowhere; 'If only we had known you were here,' they said. Nice friendly people. Mrs Daniels gave Eily a big kiss, me a lipsticky smile and put down the results of her war effort on the table in the hall – a dozen fresh brown eggs and pots of honey and jam. The shopkeepers no longer scowled when I came through the door and the off ration luxuries that had been kept for regular customers were suddenly available for me, too.

It was a week of sunshine and plenty. I loved Bernard and Eily. Bernard was a tall dark man with a military moustache which looked out of place on a face creased with thinking rather than giving commands. When he wasn't in his study writing about golf he was on the seat in the front garden counting the aeroplanes as they went to bomb France. When they returned he counted them again to see if any were missing. That's how I always think of him – sitting on the seat, his face turned upwards to the sky.

Eily fussed over me. 'You haven't sat down all morning,' was one of her favourite comments. She insisted that I rested after lunch and had a hot milky drink at night. On the last day we made a tour of the garden.

'Do you like the privet?' she asked. I admitted that I did, rather shamefacedly, it was golden, variegated, and showing signs of getting out of control.

'Good,' she replied, 'I like it too. Darwins don't. They think it's vulgar. We're Celts. We understand each other.'

I had never thought of myself as belonging to a race. I asked Erasmus,

'What are the characteristics of the Celts?'

'Short, squat, dark, and rather aggressive,' he replied. I didn't mind the unflattering description if it applied to both of us – my adored Eily and myself.

Nora welcomed us back to Boswells with open wings. There was a posy of flowers on the dressing table – violets, primroses and a few scented sprigs of Alan's precious shrubs, snipped with the secateurs, no doubt while his back was turned. Susan's Christian smile only faded when she saw our suitcases disgorging clothes over the room she had prepared.

Having had a rest from our demands Nora now seemed positively willing, almost eager, to look after Jeremy while we visited Martin Pollock and his wife in Leicester. But she became less willing and not at all eager when she heard we were going to hitch-hike there rather than go by train.

The first car or lorry with room for both of us always stopped at the sight of me, voluminous in my maternity clothes, standing on the edge of the road. It was assumed we were on our way to the nearest hospital, and we let that be the assumption until our lift was secure.

We arrived in Leicester while it was still light. Martin had found a charming house. The front garden was given over to vegetables, in accordance with the 'Dig for Victory' campaign. Beans were already shooting up in neat rows. As we walked up the path Martin and his wife, Jean, with a baby in her arms, appeared on the balcony. Framed by the Regency wrought iron they looked like a picture of the Holy family.

We had not seen each other for a couple of years. Our pleasure at being together with old friends carried us through the evening on the crest of the conversational wave until bed time, when Jean suggested I should be the one to have the first bath – the mandatory five inches in which everyone after me would wash. Martin objected. In a fretful tone he complained,

'I don't want to have my bath in the water of a pregnant woman. I think Biddy should be the one to go last.' I don't remember whether I went to bed washed or unwashed but I do remember sobbing hurt feelings into my pillow.

Nora disapproved of us hitching lifts up to Leicester and back. She didn't exactly express her disapproval in words, but I could hear it in her laugh when we got home. She wanted me to be peaceful and bovine and I simply could not oblige. I had to walk off my restless energy every day. She always accompanied me, insisting we didn't go too far and we sat down if I got puffed. I tried to explain my state of heightened awareness to her,

'The buttercups seem so bright that they hurt my eyes,' I said, 'and the birdsong is almost deafening.' Unable to relate these sensations to anything she had felt in her own pregnancies, Nora looked anxious as though concerned for my mental health.

'You really will need help after the baby arrives, two children is going to be a lot of extra work,' she said, and then after a few bars rest introduced the second subject. 'Gladys, who was nursemaid when we were at the Warren, is looking for a job.' An idea thrown at me while we sat together in a buttercup field turned out to be the main theme in a major work. Before I had time to collect my thoughts Gladys had become living menopausal flesh and blood whom I was interviewing while Nora hid behind the newspaper in the corner of the room.

It was clear from the very start that Gladys had decided the job was hers. Any questions I asked never received a straight reply but referred back to the twenty years she had spent with the Hamblyn family in Amersham.

Jeremy must have his daily walk. Of course, the Hamblyn girls always had a walk each afternoon unless it was raining or very cold, no point in taking a child out if the weather was bad. She suffered from aches and pains herself which got worse in the damp. No, she never did any cooking, Mrs Hamblyn did that, and the egg ration, they always had fried with a rasher of bacon on Friday night. She hoped the new baby would be a girl, because after twenty years of bringing up a family of girls it would seem strange at first to be looking after a baby boy, although, she conceded, flushing at the obvious, she knew they weren't really all that different from little girls.

We hadn't any idea yet of where we were going to live. After hearing all about Nanny's friends in Amersham we knew it would be wiser to look for a house in that area. How else would she spend her afternoons off and attend that chapel she had been going to for all those years?

'Would you be prepared to stay at Boswells until we are settled?'

At my tentative query Nora, who had remained noisily quiet, put down the newspaper and said,

'You remember Susan, don't you? She was Nanny at the Warren when you were nursemaid? She's still with us now.'

Glady's carefully non-commital reply told me she hadn't

enjoyed that time with Susan in charge. There was one subject
on which we might agree.

Now that everything was settled, Nora began to have mis-
givings about how I would manage the help who was coming
because I couldn't manage two babies on my own.

'Gladys was never an easy person,' she said. 'Very religious.
Puritanical. I'm not sure that she and Susan really got on and
of course living with a family all those years will make her very
set in her ways.'

All prepared to give Gladys, or Nanny, as she wanted to be
called, notice before she had arrived, I was bewildered by
Nora suddenly changing course again. It would be worth giving her a try, she said. Gladys could well be a stabilising
influence on our life and with so much shifting around Jeremy
needed security, particularly now with a new baby coming.

But *when* was the new baby coming? After prodding my
tummy Miss Dodds brought the expected date of delivery forward two weeks. I went up to stay in Wimpole Street so as to be
near the Kilburn nursing home which I had chosen because it
was cheap, had a vase of daffodils on the hall table and a matron who smiled. I was vast, like a galleon in full sail. Even
grandfather, who was half blind, noticed my size. He turned
to Andrew and mistaking him for Erasmus said,

'I think you had better be prepared for being the father of
twins, my boy.'

Miss Dodds began thinking along similar lines until an X-
ray showed just one baby curled up in my womb. Castor oil,
more castor oil, pains that began in the night had a tiresome
habit of disappearing by morning. Perhaps a bumpy ride on a
tram might do the trick, an old-fashioned remedy, but you
never know. And if that failed there would be nothing for it
except to come into the nursing home next day and prepare
for a clinical induction the following morning. Clergymen
were inducted, I knew, but what could that have to do
with me?

'The membranes are pierced with a needle and that begins
the labour,' Miss Dodds explained. This perfectly normal bar-
baric procedure determined me to let a tram do the job. I
chose a route that began in Holborn and ended outside the
hospital in Lewisham where Erasmus worked.

I hadn't told Erasmus I was coming. When he appeared in

the main hall he looked distracted rather than pleasantly surprised to see me. He said he had something important to say but wouldn't tell what it was until we were out of view of the reception desk.

'My call-up papers have arrived,' he said, 'I'm going for my medical next month.' The shock sent my hands first to my heart then to my big tummy. We had always known that one day he would have to go into the army, but not now, not when I was expecting a baby. How unfair, how terribly unfair, I sniffed and snivelled on my return journey, no longer able to relish every twist and jolt of the tram.

Back in the house I hoped to indulge myself by thrashing around on my bed in tears but Aunt Helen was preparing to entertain an assortment of guests and enlisted my help.

'There will be two of my Southwark boys,' she explained, 'and a distant cousin of mine who never utters a word.' The two Southwark boys turned out to be fully grown men, older than I, and the cousin talked non-stop throughout the meal about his experiences in the First World War. He had spent four years in the trenches and been awarded the Victoria Cross. When he finally got round to asking me about Erasmus I found it impossible not to be hypocritical.

'His call-up papers arrived today,' I said with a patriotic lilt in my voice, as though I was really glad he was soon going to be in uniform.

That night I lay awake listening to aeroplanes droning overhead. They were going to bomb Germany, part of the offensive which Churchill asserted was equivalent to the second front. The gloating account of the carnage in the newspaper next morning gave me a fleeting sense of my own unimportance. All those lives lost! All that damage done! With unusual calm I caught the bus to the nursing home. But once installed in the bedroom the other me took over. Imagination ran riot. Suppose the needle went too deep and pierced the baby's head by mistake? Impossible to stay the whole evening alone, haunted by what might go wrong. I had to get out. Now. I arranged to meet my sister and together we went to the cinema in Leicester Square.

The title of the film, *The Woman of the Year*, appeared on the screen at the exact moment that my labour began. We moved our seats back several rows to be nearer the exit, 'just in case', we explained to the usherette, who wished me 'Good Luck' when we left two hours later. These pains were genuine, not just another false alarm.

When I waddled back into the nursing home the night sister ordered me to bed.

'Fancy gallivanting off to the cinema. It would have been more sensible if you stayed here to be shaved,' she said, wielding a razor between my legs.

The all-in wrestling match lasted throughout the night with the matron's soothing smiles from the action-packed end of the bed. At five o'clock, on a soft summer's morning, Miss Dodds delivered me of a baby girl.

I cradled my daughter in my arms and thought: This is a miracle. A miracle of craftsmanship. Hair, eyelashes, neat little ears, two chubby arms and two mottled legs. Wonderful! I called her Camilla.

Now that I believed in miracles I was greedy for one more. I began not exactly praying, but rather badgering God, who in the Ministry of Miracles sat behind a desk looking very official and rather severe. There was a war on, didn't I know? Miracles were in short supply and a stockpile must be kept in reserve for the second front. A contribution to the Save the Soul fund might help. I could grease the heavenly palm by being a better person, give up making such a fuss, keep my emotions under control. I will endeavour so to do.

As if to test the strength of my resolution the siren screeched a warning immediately after my vow was made. Matron bustled into my room.

'Good gracious,' she exclaimed, 'I expected to find you completely hysterical and there you are sitting up in bed quite calm.'

After we returned to Boswells, Susan put me to an even greater test. I overheard her talking to Mrs Mason, the cook, underneath my bedroom window while I was feeding the baby.

'Is Mrs Erasmus ever going to go?' she asked, raising her voice for my benefit. Mrs Mason, who hadn't read the script, mumbled an inaudible reply. Turning up the volume, Susan continued the attack,

'They say they're looking for a house but they've been here nearly a month and they haven't found one yet. If you ask me, they're far too comfortable where they are.'

The verbal broadside scored a direct hit and I trembled, longing to retaliate. But I mustn't lose control. Tomorrow was the day of the much needed miracle.

Erasmus left after breakfast for his medical at the RAMC in Millbank. No sooner had he gone than I knew there was something I had to say, running down the corridor I called over the banisters,

'Don't forget to mention your motorbike accident!' But he was already half way across the hall and I knew he wouldn't hear because his fractured skull had left him deaf in one ear.

My head ached with wanting each telephone bell to be for me. When at last I heard Erasmus's voice at the end of the wire I found myself thanking God before I really knew what the miracle was. Nora, seeing my relief, exclaimed,

'I had no idea it meant so much to you.' When Alan came home that evening I witnessed her telling him the news. It was a conversation piece stripped of everything except words.

'Erasmus has failed his medical.'

'Is he ill?'

'No. It's his fractured skull.'

'Oh.'

'I don't know what he'll do now.'

'Neither do I.'

We did. There was a job waiting for him at Guys Hospital. He joined Dr Grant's research team working on shock. And then as though that wasn't enough beneficience, God handed out more bounty in the form of a house. Not just an ordinary three up, two down semi-detached, but a small Georgian farmhouse with oak beams, tiled floors, surrounded by a cherry orchard, and most conveniently placed within walking distance of my mother, a short drive from Boswells and most important of all, near enough to Amersham for Nanny to visit her friends.

Life now not only had a present and a past but a future as well. We left Boswells full of hope and surrounded by goodies from the farm which Nora bestowed on us with her usual generosity. We were happy. Even Nanny ended the cold war with Susan by giving her a glacial smile when they said goodbye.

11

Soon after settling into Little Bois Farm Mrs Hamblyn's presence began to be felt with Nanny as her medium giving endless advice. 'Mrs Hamblyn always bottled fruit at this time of year.' So we brought Kilner jars, filled the kitchen with steam, burnt our fingers and bottled fruit. 'Mrs Hamblyn always made jam.' There was an extra sugar ration for that, didn't I know? Soon jars of marrow jam and blackberry jelly stood beside the bottle of plums and greengages in the larder. Thanks to Mrs Hamblyn I learned to make a fatless sponge, which sounded like a contradiction in terms and tasted delicious. Scones had to be mastered because Mrs Hamblyn liked to have them every day for tea. She baked them in batches in order to save electricity, so I did, too, to save gas.

'Did Mrs Hamblyn keep chickens?' I asked. No. Mrs Hamblyn's garden was devoted to flowers, a blaze of colour, always something in bloom. . . .

'We are going to keep chickens,' I announced, 'and *I* am going to be the one who collects the eggs.'

'Not at this time of year, you won't' retorted Nanny, 'because laying has practically ceased.' I measured up for a chicken run but the wire netting remained in a roll. Our permanent home turned out to be a temporary abode. We were on the move again.

The medical unit at Guy's Hospital to which Erasmus was now attached needed more cases of severe injury. Newcastle-on-Tyne, with its mining and shipping accidents, could provide a continuous supply. So to Newcastle they must go. I went up to London to see my husband off on the train. Feeling bereft, miserable, frightened and spurned I met Dr Grant and his right hand man, Dr Reeve, for the first time. Cold-blooded scientists, I decided they were – an emotional display would do them good, make them a little more human, perhaps? They cringed in the corner of the compartment while I sobbed with abandon. Someone else witnessed my distress. A woman, living up to the WVS badge on her tweed coat, felt obliged to comfort the poor little wife whose husband had gone off to the war. She put her arms round me, led me towards the canteen, and was fumbling with her purse, all set to buy me a cup of tea when she discovered my husband was a civilian, going no further than Newcastle, where I would join him as soon as I could.

Nora didn't want me to follow Erasmus up to Newcastle, even when he found a house opposite the Royal Victoria Infirmary where the unit was installed she still opposed the idea. Why couldn't I be like other war-time wives, stay put with the children and see my husband when he came on leave? For such an upheaval I needed Nora's approval and only when I had secured that did I break the news that my bottle fruit, jars of jam and hoarded tins were coming with me. Nanny, understandably aggrieved soon became grimly resigned to leaving her Amersham friends. Sometimes I think her life was lived for the sake of an obituary in the local press, which would go like this,

'Glady's Ames was a true Christian who never shirked her duty. Regardless of danger or suffering she always put others before herself.'

Letting the cottage provided a little light relief when the estate agent sent me the actor Valentine Dyall as a prospective tenant. He wore a large brimmed black hat and came through the door quoting Housman,
'Loveliest of trees, the cherry now . . .' He was much too good looking for my comfort. I became acutely conscious of my grubby apron and bare, hairy legs. Before committing himself to a nine month lease he needed to talk to his wife and then come again for further inspection. This time I prepared for his visit and put on a lightweight crepe skirt and a chiffon blouse, clothes totally unsuitable for the time of year. Nanny saw what I was wearing, heard the warmth of our greeting, and smelled the coffee we spent over an hour drinking in the kitchen. After he had gone with a theatrical wave of his hat and still quoting Housman,
'About the woodlands I will go to see the cherry hung with snow,' Nanny withdrew into the sitting-room to have a long conversation on the telephone with the door firmly shut so I

couldn't hear what she said. I had let Little Bois Farm to the most charming tenant. I almost wished I could stay behind as part of the fittings and furniture that went with the house.

That Christmas we were scattered. Jeremy was with my mother and Erasmus was at the hospital, working. His boss, Dr Grant, ignored public holidays, whether religiously significant or not. Alone in the kitchen I ate a slice of Spam before giving the baby her two o'clock feed.

Nanny, by all accounts, enjoyed herself more than any of us. She arrived in Newcastle with a storm force smile and Jeremy in tow. All the shops closed for the New Year, not just one day but a whole week. My newly stocked store cupboard came into its own; we were glad now for all the food I'd brought up with me on the train.

Our house resembled the Novacastrians with a plain exterior concealing a heart of gold. It was extremely livable in, with well-proportioned comfortable rooms that got a lot of sun when the clouds disappeared; mostly the days were grey and the nights chilly. We gave Nanny and the children the best rooms and slept in the back extension, which being above an unused workshop had more than its fair share of outside walls and faced North over the town moor.

Nanny received letters every day with an Amersham postmark. Through the Baptist chapel she met kindred spirits who provided a social life although they could never compensate for her Amersham friends. We, less quick off the mark, gradually got to know the people living in Claremont Place. Our immediate neighbours seemed at first a cut above us with their snowy white carpets, Picasso prints and absence of any children. Next to them was a small boy with a penchant for earthworms. He always had a handful wriggling in and out of his fingers and given half a chance, so rumour had it, they would end up in his mouth. Later on he became a distinguished surgeon. When visiting a patient in a London hospital I recognised his name above the bed. There was a couple from Cambridge, kindred spirits until I caused offence by bringing my knitting with me when they invited us to dinner. John Bunyan at number nine had the cachet of an easily recognisable name but he had also earned a reputation in his own right with his Bunyan bag treatment for burns. The bohemian existence led by a zoologist and his wife contrasted sharply with the respectable couples living in the row.

When Professor Spence called I thought he was just another doctor from the hospital doing his duty by welcoming us to Newcastle. He had unbrushed greying hair and a lined face which was neither handsome nor plain and therefore I classed as 'interesting'. After shaking hands he asked,

'What is your background?' and when I answered promptly,

'Left wing Quakerism,' he nodded approvingly and sat down. If I had replied 'Borstal and Holloway' I wonder what his reaction would have been. More approving, perhaps, since he was a loner, against the system, unacceptable to the medical establishment until he was knighted for his great discovery – mother love.

James Spence spent years of research to show that a child recovered quicker from an illness the more the mother was around. Contrary to what the Matron said, a mother in a children's ward was a positive benefit. Before making a diagnosis it was worth listening to what she had to say. He fought and won a battle over restricted visiting hours and revolutionised a hospital building to allow a mother to stay near her sick child. Much of what he was struggling to achieve then is accepted as commonplace now. It took a long time for diehard pockets of resistance to disappear. As late as the 1950s some doctors still maintained that mother love was all right, but penicillin was better.

We became friends with this strange eccentric whose crumpled shirt and dislodged tie set him apart from the smooth consultants at the hospital. He was always willing to drop in on his way to work. I used him unmercifully, demanding his advice if my children were the least bit off colour. Often his advice reinforced what I wanted to do – cuddle him, give him sweets, leave the light on. Let him fill the bed with Dinky cars.

Early on I acquired a charwoman by the simple method of stopping a likely looking candidate in the street and asking her to work for me. Mrs Hutchinson turned out to be a great success. Unlike our lodger who, searching for somewhere to live, knocked on my door and inveigled me into allowing him to occupy a room at the top of the house. A great mistake.

He consulted Erasmus about a cure for his smelly feet,

complained of the children's table manners and demanded a pudding every night. He was always late with the rent, which he called 'filthy lucre'.

When the air raids started, the siren didn't wake him. We let him sleep on and he never became part of our routine drill. First wail, out of bed. Dressing gown, bedroom slippers, carry Jeremy down to the dining-room and put Camilla in her pram under the stairs. Then we sat round the table as though at a seance, waiting for something to happen. Most of the crashing and banging came from the guns on the town moor. It was impossible to guage how far the danger was away and I half expected to find in the morning that the houses on either side were rubble. One evening, after a hospital function, we ran home with the shrapnel falling around us like giant hailstones; a group of people had gathered under our porch for safety and were watching a fight going on overhead.

'Come on ... get him ... get him ... get him. ...'

'Don't forget he's someone's husband or son,' I said, unable to explain when they turned on me that I wanted neither side to win or lose; as in a tennis match I was always happiest with a draw.

Dr Grant and Dr Reeve spent their day off walking in the country. Soon they asked us to join them and the four of us caught the train early in the morning, not to return until it was nearly dark.

These Monday walks became the focal point of my week. Dr Grant and Erasmus strode ahead in silence while I and Dr Reeve, who quickly became Basil, lagged behind discussing 'life'. Undeterred by painful joints and aching muscles I trudged through bracken, up hills and down valleys. After a particularly arduous rainy walk my legs were so stiff that I had difficulty in getting out of the train.

'You shouldn't be like that at your age,' Dr Grant said, 'Is there anything the matter?'

'Nothing.' I went on saying nothing was the matter until red lumps appeared on my shins. Then I consulted a doctor post haste. I was ill. I must go into hospital as soon as a bed was free and meanwhile I was to be treated as an invalid at home. No sitting up in bed peeling the potatoes – I must rest. Easier said than done with Nanny's incredulous face and the lodger demanding pudding.

When Nora heard of our crisis she dropped everything and travelled up by train to Newcastle. She insisted I had supper in bed and brought me up a bowl of fish soup. I have never known Nora cook anything before or since and how she managed to buy the fish I shall never know; in many a queue at the fishmongers I waited for over an hour, counting the nits in the hair of the woman in front of me as we shuffled nearer our goal, a piece of rock salmon or the remnants of cod, and here was Nora, soon after her arrival on her very first day, creating a memorable fish soup.

I spent the next day in my dressing gown, nipping out of bed when no-one was looking, catching up on the household chores. The lodger found me cleaning out the bath, snatched the cloth from my hand exclaiming,

'You shouldn't be doing that,' and completed the job himself.

Tiresome little man, I thought, why couldn't he be consistently unpleasant so that I could justify my dislike of him? And then, to increase my guilt, he offered the loan of his portable radio, a great sacrifice on his part which I knew I should refuse but accepted with doubtful grace.

That radio played an important part in my hospital routine. Punctually at ten thirty every morning two young nurses bustled in to my room, switched on their favourite programme, 'Music while you work,' and to the strains of 'A kiss is still a kiss', and 'When the lights come on again', they gave me a blanket bath and made my bed.

I enjoyed receiving letters of commiseration until Erasmus received one too commiserating with him for having such an ailing wife as me. Geoffrey Keynes, without examining the patient, gave his medical opinion to Nora who raised the alarm that the red lumps could be a reaction to TB. Erasmus passed the message to my doctor who sent me to have an X-ray. My lungs were clear. After further prevarication a diagnosis was made –a streptococcal infection caused by my tonsils which had been removed when I was three years old.

Nanny paid me duty visits. While the children romped around the room she sat in a chair stifling yawns and looking utterly exhausted. Clearly she deserved the rest as much as I did. The treatment, large doses of aspirin, caused only slight discomfort with a buzzing in the head. The hours passed pleasantly, knitting, reading, listening to music, until the dreaded swish of the black-out curtain covered the strip of sky outside my bricked-up window.

Most nights there were air-raid warnings and I, complying with the doctor's order of complete bed rest, lay sweating between the sheets, knowing that the agitated feet outside in the corridor were running to find safety in the basement shelter. Dr Grant, not such a cold-blooded scientist after all, understood my fear of being alone. As soon as the siren sounded he or Basil Reeve would come in to my room to keep me company. Generally it was Basil who came and while the guns blasted death into the air we talked about life until the siren sounded the all clear.

When the red lumps disappeared I went home, and having lost touch with the seasons, found it quite a shock to see that Spring had arrived. Soon it was warm enough for us to accept invitations from Aunt Helen's friends, who lived in a large country house with maids as starched and well-pressed as the table linen. The cloakrooms were always worth a visit; antiquated, polished mahogany lavatory seats and porcelain pans decorated with flowers, signed by the artist 'Shanks'.

At the end of June Nanny went on a protracted, well-deserved holiday and Nora ordered, blandished, bribed, I don't know which, her cook, Mrs Mason, to come up to prevent me from what she called 'overdoing it'. Nanny, by courtesy of Mrs Hamblyn, had been far more use in the kitchen than she had ever been in the nursery, while Mrs Mason, whose cooking was heavy and unimaginative, showed a natural knack with children which amply compensated for her soups, always the same shade of brown, and stodgy puddings, only appreciated by the lodger. Jeremy was forever seeking out Mrs Mason in the kitchen, sitting on her knee, asking her to sing hymns 'What is a bosom fly?' –and I felt far more at ease leaving Camilla with her than I ever felt with Nanny in charge. All of which proved Professor Spence's point – practical people like cooks make better child minders than the trained professionals. In this short-term domestic arrangement we relaxed, let things slide, enjoyed our freedom to such an extent that by the time we travelled south I was pregnant again. We were delighted.

Nora and her sister, Ruth, prepared a wonderful welcome for us at Little Bois Farm which had been left in perfect order by the glamorous tenant. They had filled every available bowl with fruit, and vases of flowers were dotted all over the house. I kept quiet about my pregnancy, having decided an early announcement made the nine months seem unnecessarily long. Wise to the dangers of fatty foods I followed a careful diet which consisted mainly of pea soup made from the pods. When the well-travelled Kilner jars had been replenished and enough jam made to last us through the year we said goodbye to Little Bois Farm, regretting we would never see the cherry blossom hanging on the bough.

As soon as we got off the train at Newcastle I took a deep breath of the tainted air and thought how good it was to be back. Claremont Place had ceased to be a rented house full of hideous furniture and faded pictures of highland cattle. It was home and I was accepted as part of the community. The couple next door immediately invited us round for breakfast and throughout the day neighbours called with offers of help, which included drinking my coffee while bringing me up to date with the latest gossip.

A dismembered body had been found in an unused drain on the town moor and a precious gentian stolen from the vicar's front garden. The Bunyan boy, held responsible for the latter crime, was now branded as a delinquent by those who, in spite of his mother's protests, swore they had witnessed him picking it. The zoologist wife at the end of the row had renounced domesticity and embarked on a university course. She had even bought herself a student's skirt, grey, much too short, and a V-necked pullover. Ridiculous, at her age! And there hadn't been an air raid warning for weeks, probably something to do with the second front, how or why, no-one knew that was what I really wanted to hear.

The student wife, under the guise of public spiritidness, started a scheme whereby we mothers took it in turns to look after each other's children for one morning a week. The rota functioned well at first, but when the student wife found the university expected her to produce written work she opted out of her share of the scheme. Others found excuses too and soon the children gathered in our house which Nanny bore with tight-lipped charity until one child, with a double dose of original sin, used the plasticine to model an enormous phallus. End of group activity.

An important change came to the unit that autumn with the arrival of Ludwig Wittgenstein who started working there as a lab boy. From my bedroom window I watched him and Basil Reeve walking across the town moor. By their bent heads I could tell they were discussing philosophy. My brief innings with waffling about life was over. When Erasmus brought Wittgenstein home for tea I made no special effort. I knew about Wittgenstein's simple tastes, how he chose to live in a single room, furnished with only a deck chair and a bed. He was perfectly at ease with this family occasion. Home-made jam, a Mrs Hamblyn cake, Nanny and Jeremy sitting at the table and Camilla in her high chair. He helped himself to an enormous slice of cake, spread it with jam, and wolfed it down in one go. He then turned his attention to Jeremy's books, going through them with care. Having selected 'The Little Boy and his House' he started a unilateral discussion on its merits. We couldn't understand a word of what he said but we knew he had chosen the best one, although not necessarily for the reasons we thought. The philosophical message in the book was beyond our grasp.

A peace-time friend came to stay, with her baby. She behaved very much as I behaved at Boswells, creating chaos in the carefully prepared room when she arrived.

'I'll eat absolutely everything,' she assured me. I took her at her word and produced a risotto for supper.

'Oh dear, I don't like Spam,' she said, 'and onions don't like me.'

She picked out the main ingredients and left them on the side of her plate.

'But I adore rice,' she insisted. Just as well, I thought, that's all you're going to get.

She never offered to lend me a hand but was ever willing to relieve Nanny of her duties.

'You're an absolute treasure,' I overheard her say, 'what a pity you're only a mother's help.'

She filled saucers with cigarette stubs and smoked in the bedroom, ignoring the baby's cough.

'Just teething,' she said, until the baby began to choke, when she demanded a doctor.

'Not a GP. I must have the best for my baby.'

Professor Spence with his frayed shirt, moth-eaten pullover and direct manner was not the smooth consultant she wanted. He was equally disenchanted by her. Their mutual antipathy alarmed me, because I had never seen Professor Spence in that light before. He was off-hand and rude. No smile. No charm. He admonished the mother for smoking and left. The baby recovered and my friend, no longer a friend, took him home at the end of the week. That visit had a salutary effect.

I benefited from the bad example, became tidier. 'What's happened,' Nanny exclaimed, 'everything's folded neatly – usually I have to hunt for the clothes.' There were other repercussions too. We had to give Nanny a substantial rise. How else could we persuade her that she was not a mother's help?

I'd witnessed Professor Spence when he disapproved and now dreaded the same behaviour being meted out to me. When Camilla began to walk she had a peculiar gait, and instead of consulting Professor Spence I relied on the hospital's orthopaedic registrar for an opinion.

'Just a plump child,' he said, 'there's nothing wrong with her.'

He made me feel I was a fussy mother. I was glad I hadn't bothered Professor Spence.

Preparation for Christmas began with a lot of chopping up of ingredients that don't usually find their way into the Christmas fare. Carrots, turnips, prunes and marrow jam eked out the slender extra allocation of dried fruit. Presents had to be bought and despatched in good time. Cards of darning wool for Joan; dish cloths for my sister with directions of how to convert them to a summer blouse; shammy leather dusters made a welcome gift too, although I can't remember why. Gloves perhaps? The main bulk of my presents consisted of well-fingered fudge made by the children on a rainy afternoon from the sugar ration supplied by the unborn baby's green ration book. Everything was wrapped up, labelled with best wishes for Christmas and the New Year, and tied with plaited embroidery thread.

A Christmas tree, bought in the market and propped up in the corner of the sitting-room, looked very convincing with the fairy lights, borrowed from the hospital. We added blobs of cotton wool and strips of crinkled silver cigarette packet paper, as no shop sold any decorations.

Nanny, with memories of more affluent Christmasses, kept wondering what Mrs Hamblyn would say if she could see her now.

'Such wonderful stocking fillers the Hamblyn children always had,' she said, watching us late on Christmas Eve stuff clothes pegs, lumps of coalite and bars of soap into socks that the children had hung up at the end of their beds.

Having no expectations, Jeremy and Camilla were delighted with everything they got. Although Erasmus had to go to work in the morning he came home for the ersatz Christmas dinner. The whole day had a traditional flavour, with the traditional exhaustion when we finally cleared up the wrapping paper and went to bed.

The new year brought hope that 1944 would see the long-awaited second front and the end of the war. Behind this spirit of optimism there was still a nagging worry over the way Camilla walked. It was as though she had one leg shorter than the other. Nanny and I laid her on the floor and measured her legs, they were the same length, but we were still worried.

We called in the orthopaedic registrar twice more; each time we got the same reply, nothing was wrong. Camilla walked like that because she was a plump child. I was definitely classed as a fussy mother.

12

I looked forward to the expected date of delivery, April the fourth, not only for the excitement of having a new baby but as an opportunity to get into bed and have a good rest. Providing four meals a day became increasingly irksome as my pregnancy advanced.

Nora, with long distance sensitivity, offered me the services of Mrs Mason again which meant there was a cook as well as a nanny, a monthly nurse and a charwoman to see me through my home confinement. Right on schedule, without any drama, the waters broke at five o'clock in the morning. We went downstairs to the kitchen, lit a fire, made tea which neither of us wanted to drink and filled in time before the nurse arrived.

Quietly efficient, she prepared the room, revealed the mystery of the sterile drum, rubbed my back when the pains began while talking about the second front. When was it going to start? Would there be singing and dancing in the streets? And what if it failed? Another defeat described as a strategic withdrawal.

Late in the afternoon the great moment came, after many brief encounters the final assignation with my doctor. The birth of Phyllida was like a beautifully danced *pas de deux* or two voices singing in perfect unison. The doctor said it had been his most enjoyable confinement and only Mrs Mason was disappointed. She complained that the house had been quiet as a tomb.

The birth of Phyllida was literally a happy event which left me in a state of post-puerperal elation. Nora on hearing the news that she had a grandaughter called Phyllida objected to the name considering it too fancy, particularly as we already had a Camilla. Erasmus hurt that this should be his mother's response to an excited telephone call was comforted by my laugh. 'Let's call her Gillian after my sister.' I said. 'Phyllida can be her second name. We can always switch later on.'

187

Which is exactly what we did.

Nothing could wipe the ecstatic smile off my face. I still smiled when Nanny, just after Mrs Mason and the monthly nurse had left, announced that she would like to go soon, too. Her parents were getting old and needed her but of course she would wait until I found someone else. The labour exchange heard the smile in my voice and sent me the least employable people on their books. A middle-aged enuretic, a teenage psychopath, a twenty-two year old who couldn't stop crying and then Kathleen, with a thin narrow face and bright sub human eyes. On June 6 I phoned Kathleen's previous employer for a reference and was told she had only been there three weeks. 'She's really pretty useless, practically feeble minded. Can't even put the shoes on the right feet,' and then as an afterthought,

'By the way, it has started.' And that was how I heard the news of the second front.

I think even the most confirmed atheist said prayers that day. The streets were deserted. Everyone was indoors listening to the wireless. I found waiting for the news claustrophobic. I wandered around an empty store trying on clothes and discarding them until to appease the assistant I bought a dress and a silly little hat with a veil and a rose. Displacement behaviour, perhaps?

Two days later, John Bunyan and his wife gave a party to celebrate our foothold in Europe, Too early to celebrate such a precarious foothold, I thought, but we accepted the invitation nevertheless. Most of Claremont Place came to the party, with a sprinkling of people I didn't know. I was introduced to a youngish orthopaedic surgeon whose flirtatious repartee went straight to my head like the champagne I didn't drink. Our hostess, seeing how much we enjoyed each other's company, did her best to separate us but she never succeeded. We were still in the same corner of the room by the time the party ended when he gave me his card with a smile that convinced me we would see each other again.

When we got home it was already late but I couldn't rest until I'd spoken to him on the telephone.

'I'm worried about my daughter's walking,' I said, 'I didn't want to talk shop at the party but I would be very grateful if you'd look at her.' Delighted. Of course he was delighted. An appointment was made for the next day. I wore my new dress and my silly little hat to walk across the town moor with Erasmus and Camilla in her pram to his house that had a brass plate beside the door.

He looked different in his white coat, avoiding my eyes as we shook hands. He watched Camilla running round the consulting room and said,

'I suspect congenital dislocation of the hip,' and before I had absorbed the full implications of that he was preening himself because the X-ray confirmed his suspicions.

'She'll have to go into hospital for manipulation,' he said, 'and be put in a plaster case.' A plaster cast? The words screamed inside my head.

'She won't be able to walk, but they quickly adapt.' Camilla wasn't 'they'; she was my adorable little girl who loved exploring the house, opening cupboards, jumping up and down the stairs.

'If the blood supply to the femur hasn't been cut off it will only take about eighteen months. The chances of avascular necrosis are one in five.'

I glanced at Erasmus, he was trying to smile, to be reassuring, while horror after horror unfolded.

So perhaps my mother had not been so wrong after all. Genes. Whose hateful genes were to blame for this? I must never, never, never, let Erasmus know what I thought, it would hurt him too much. Crimson in the face with self-control we began our walk back across the town moor and before we reached home all my bitterness spewed out in a venomous tirade of reproach. We had been married six years and that evening we had our first major row.

Two days later Camilla ran out of the house, a happy, smiling child and returned forty-eight hours later a desperate captive, pushing at the plaster and screaming,

'I want to get out.' The hospital, expecting casualties from France, had to have her bed vacated as soon as possible and the nurses were too fraught to give any advice on how to manage her at home.

Mrs Hutchinson, my charwoman, said I had aged overnight. Nanny, equally comforting, said my worrying was upsetting the baby's milk. Friends called and invariably said the wrong thing too. I went for a walk and who should drive past but Professor Spence. He recognised my deep despair, stopped the car, opened the door and said,

'Get in.' In a quiet leafy square, holding my hand, he listened to my miserable outpourings.

'Why didn't you tell me?' he asked.

'I didn't want you to think I was a fussy mother.'

'If there weren't fussy mothers there wouldn't be any children,' he replied. Memorable words.

We took our stricken faces down to Boswells and threw our unhappiness into Nora's outstretched arms. She visibly and audibly suffered too. Suggestions from her sounded like criticisms, especially when my small frame was blamed for Camilla's hip. Our crisis could not be contained. It spread through the whole house, penetrating the green baize door where Susan tyrannised a skeleton staff. Now that there was less help we, in the dining-room, withdrew after each meal to the butler's pantry and did a share of the washing-up. As I was passing a pile of plates through to the kitchen, Susan appeared on the other side of the hatch, took a deep breath, and delivered a well rehearsed speech,

'When I think of what her ladyship went through with Miss Joan,' she said, enunciating each word clearly in her ladyship's accent, 'all those operations! And so many disappointments. She always showed such courage and managed to remain so cheerful.'

Nora worried that Camilla would be spoiled, that the baby would be neglected, that Jeremy would resent all the attention going elsewhere, but I shrugged off these worries; it was enough to get through each day.

Nanny left, Kathleen arrived, the former in tears, the latter all smiles and what might have been a trauma was just a rather tiresome change-over.

I was scarcely aware of what was happening in France until the liberation of Paris pin-pointed the date that Camilla went for a check-up at the Wingfield hospital in Oxford. More X-rays, a different head above the white coat but the same grave expression as Mr Girdlestone said,

'The hip has slipped out of place. She'll have to come into hospital and have another manipulation.' He gave us a few seconds to recover and then offered us a crumb of comfort.

'I'll put her in a different plaster. It will be better for her and easier for you to manage.'

The crumb of comfort turned out to be quite a substantial snack. In the new plaster which had an iron bar from ankle to ankle she could sit up, have the tangles in her hair combed out, and wear her pretty dresses.

She soon developed her own method of mobility and every day, for one hour after tea, she slid around the room on her bottom, pulling out the books from the shelves and exploring the cupboards.

Gradually the different demands of the children met, merged and integrated into an established routine. Kathleen helped by being prepared to do anything she was told. Although Boswells maintained a superficial calm with the gong booming us into meals and Alan escaping to his study via the cellar every night, there had been a noticeable lack of weekend guests during this agitated time. Now that we were slightly better organised Alan invited Hugh Mackintosh and Sammy Cook to stay.

Nora disapproved of Alan's two friends. Not only were they members of the Savile Club which counted against them from the start, but they also had that dubious quality – charm. They talked a lot, laughed loudly and were God's gift to children. Hugh had a fascinating store of stories and poems to amuse Jeremy. Sammy Cook flirted with Camilla – after a few gins he insisted on waltzing round the hall with her, and singing at the top of his voice: 'If you were the only girl in the world,' which delighted me and embarrassed some of the company.

Hugh was recovering from an illness which, because it was unspecified, convinced Nora it must be due to drinking too much at the notorious Savile. She became suspicious that the medicine he took was really alcohol, a large dose three times a day after meals. I offered to keep *cave* on the stairs while she nipped into his room to sniff the bottle on his dressing-table. It was rather an anti-climax when she recognised a remedy for indigestion, but the light hearted incident improved the atmosphere.

At the beginning of September Aunt Helen brought her father down to Boswells to celebrate his ninety-ninth birthday. In spite of his great age the darling man decided to smooth our passage at the Wingfield Hospital and he sent off a letter in his spidery handwriting, asking Mr Girdlestone to take special care of his grand-daughter, Camilla. By return of post came a charming reply, but no amount of charm could alter the X-ray at our next visit, which showed a darkening at the head of the femur. Avascular necrosis or Perthe's disease, either name, the result would be the same – eighteen month's treatment extended to three years.

That evening we walked up to the pub at the Lee where more gloom awaited us. The guarded report on the wireless of the Arnheim disaster silenced the usually lively bar and turned the locals into zombies. They could only utter two words as they listened to the news: Poor buggers. Poor buggers. Poor buggers. The troops had failed to meet up with supplies and the war, which might have ended by Christmas, was destined now to drag on until the spring.

We drove back to Newcastle in fine style, Lady Darwin having expressed her sympathy in a most practical way, by lending us her car, the grey Daimler. Before we left, Alan paid an unexpected visit to me in my bedroom. He was wearing his dark, civil servant's suit, well-cut but shabby. He stood looking out of the window and I can see the back of his cropped gingery head now.

'I wish you wouldn't go,' he said, 'it would be so much better if you stayed on here.'

'Why? I must be with Erasmus.'

He gave one of his expressive sniffs, muttered 'I suppose so,' and said goodbye. A surprisingly affectionate goodbye.

I decided that my work from now on would be to persuade Camilla that her life in plaster was as good as it had been before but in fact it was *she* who persuaded *me* that that was the case. Her cheerful acceptance of her restricted life set an example to us all.

Dr Grant's puritanical reign ended that autumn when Eric Bywaters took over the running of the unit. Full of zing after a year in America Eric demanded whisky when I offered him cocoa. He preferred more sophisticated pleasures than hearty walks in the country. We went to pubs and once I wore my long-sleeved silk dress for dinner at the Station Hotel. He greeted Camilla with a burst of enthusiasm, a welcome change to the usual gush-slush.

'What a wonderful contraption,' he exclaimed and got down on his knees to see how the iron bar and the plaster cast worked.

Injuries from flying bombs soon called Erasmus and Eric back to London. We gave a farewell party, crowding fifty friends into our sitting-room. It was Eric's idea that drinks should be laced with lab alcohol. Professor Spence (I could never bring myself to call him James or Jimmy) said goodbye to me in the environment that suited us best – the nursery where the children were asleep. We packed up the car in the numbing darkness next morning and left Newcastle at dawn. Jeremy expected the long journey to be over before we had crossed the Tyne.

While we were away, Hilda had become engaged to John Padel. He was tall, immensely musical and so erudite that I was sure he dreamed in Latin or Greek. Nora, obviously pleased with her prospective son-in-law, said,

'They'll have lovely, long-legged children.' I suddenly felt threatened by these future Anglo-Saxons who would outstrip my short legged Celts in a race for their grandmother's affection.

We had already had our own party and now, less than a week later, there was a pre-wedding party for Hilda and John at Wimpole Street. Professional caterers provided mushy pastes on circles of fried bread and so much champagne that Mrs Mason got drunk and Alan, a bit tottery himself, had to help her into the car for the journey home.

A white Christmas followed by a thaw before the temperature dropped again produced dramatic weather for Hilda's wedding day. There's a photo of the bride, standing on the lawn; she looks like a snow goddess in her long white dress flowing into the white ground, with haw frost clinging to the trees as a glittering backcloth.

Shortly after the wedding, Grandfather died, and the 'death of Sir Thomas Barlow' was announced on the wireless with an account of his distinguished career, and how he had been physician to Queen Victoria. Nora took a rather bracing line about the death of her father-in-law. He had had a good life, she said, and if he had lived to be a hundred years old all the vulgar fuss about his having reached the century would have been intolerable.

The family turned out in full force for the funeral service in Wendover and came back to Boswells afterwards for the ritual baked-meats. I found the occasion very moving and was thoroughly subdued by the black ties and *sotto voce* conversation until a most bizarre sight emerged from the school-room where the children had been told to stay. Holding the baby's pot at arm's length to avoid its smelly contents, Kathleen steered her way across the hall, with a series of chirpy 'Excuse me, please.'

When she reached the cloakroom an excessive amount of plug pulling and scraping of lavatory brush succeeded in silencing the astonished company.

Acutely embarrassed, I vented my anger first on the idiot girl and then sought out Nora ready to grovel with apologies, only to find a reaction I had never expected.

'Grandfather wouldn't have minded,' she assured me, 'he was always greatly in favour of bowel evacuation.' She laughed at her own joke and then added a little anecdote about the earth closets he had had specially installed in Boswells when it was built.

'He had some funny idea about returning to the ground what had been taken out of it,' she said.

I often felt that inside the serious Nora there was a frivolous Nora wanting to get out, and it is possible she felt the same about me, only in reverse. How else can I explain her prophetic remark,

'One day, Biddy, you'll write a novel.' Nora and I spent many evenings alone together while our husbands were in London –Erasmus dealing with flying bomb casualties, Alan playing bridge at the Savile. We knitted, listening to the wireless; every night the nine o'clock news and *Itma* on Thursdays. We knitted while Nora read aloud. Her favourite choice was *Pride and Prejudice* which she almost knew by heart. She preferred the flighty Lydia to the serious minded Elisabeth – another sign of her *alter ego* perhaps?

Often we knitted and just chatted about people. High level gossip, because Nora never let it sink too low. Once Mrs Hamblyn of fatless sponge fame cropped up in the conversation.

'She always had such fun,' Nora told me. Fun with all those

batches of scones? No, fun with her husband.

'I'll never forget the time I called and found them sitting over their breakfast at ten o'clock. They were talking.' Clearly it was not the late breakfast she envied but the talking.

Very occasionally she mentioned her work. That took second place in a demanding household in which we played a major part. When she finished writing her introduction to *The Voyage of the Beagle* I suggested she should dedicate the book to her grandchildren – 'who nearly made this work impossible.' That was too near the truth. She didn't smile although the corners of her mouth turned up.

Nora's mouth never drooped into a sulk; at the worst it went into a straight line. When I asked her which of her children she liked best, that straight line replied,

'I'm not going to tell even *you* that.' I had gone too far. Broken the rules.

And she should never have said what she did say about the death of my eldest brother. I'd been bragging about my childhood, how wonderfully free it had been.

'Too free perhaps,' said Nora, and then came the punch below the belt, 'if there had been someone responsible in charge that accident in the sand dunes would never have happened.'

My children were beginning to want their freedom. I could no longer be sure they would stay in the school-room if my back was turned. I wished Alan's precious ceramics were not left lying all over the place but kept under lock and key. He never fussed about these unique and beautiful objects which represented great epochs of Chinese history and culture. They were there for people to enjoy. One day the enjoyment was extended to a one year old who having crawled into the dining-room discovered a pair of sixth century dancing girls in a cupboard at floor level. She had her chubby hand wedged in the crook of a fragile arm when I discovered her. After many years I plucked up courage to confess that these priceless figures had been used as playthings. Alan only smiled. His chief concern was that I had been so worried.

At the beginning of April Camilla became ill. Kathleen hadn't noticed the feverish face and heavy eyes when she carried her into breakfast. By lunchtime she had become so listless that Nora agreed the doctor should be called. He prescribed a new drug –sulphathiazole, a little pill which I had difficulty in persuading her to swallow. When the gong boomed for tea I tucked her up warmly and went downstairs to the dining-room to tell Nora I couldn't eat anything.

'Have just a cup,' she said, and I sat down at the table, took a sip and then was seized with such panic that I jumped up, ran out of the door and up the stairs two at a time, and into the room where Camilla lay rigid in bed, her face navy blue and froth like ectoplasm cascading out of her mouth and on to the pillow. SHE IS HAVING A REACTION TO SULPHA-THIAZOLE. My instant diagnosis was in capital letters against the lining of my head. I lifted her out of the bed and tore along the corridor shouting 'Nora!' In the study I laid her on the floor, nursing her stiff little torso in my arms while Nora juggled with telephone books. The doctor, Erasmus, the district nurse. . . . HELP! Kathleen's inane smile and Susan's distraught face appeared in the doorway. What could they do to help? A mustard bath? with legs in plaster? No. Her body suddenly went limp and her head fell back into my lap.

'She's gone,' I said, 'keep the children at the end of the house.'

I prayed, I swear I prayed, and my prayers helped Camilla with those long deep breaths as her colour changed and she slowly regained consciousness. We were still in the study when the doctor, Erasmus and the district nurse arrived all together. Her temperature under her arm was 106.5.

She had had a convulsion, nothing to worry about really, just a reaction to the high fever, children often did that sort of thing. The same sequence of events, fever sulphathiazole, convulsion, occurred two months later and in between these two convulsions peace was declared.

I took the children up to the Round Hill, lit a fire, and ceremoniously burnt a piece of black-out material in the flames. That evening Nora and I sat with our knitting, listening to the broadcast of the jubilant crowds outside Buckingham Palace.

'The war isn't over yet,' she said, and she might have added, 'My son is in the Far East.' Her worry about Thomas's safety she had always kept to herself. There had been pleasure when his letters arrived and even greater pleasure when he came home on leave. I looked at her face and asked,

'Shall I turn the wireless off?'

'Please do,' Nora replied, 'I hope there isn't going to be too much gloating over our victory.'

When Camilla had her third convulsion I said,

'I'm going to write a letter to *The Lancet* and tell them sulphathiazole can be a dangerous drug and Camilla should be given aspirin instead.'

'You'll make a fool of yourself if you do,' I was told, so I wrote to Professor Spence instead.

A prompt reply announced his arrival the following week with a request to stay overnight if that was convenient. Susan prepared the spare room for him and I arranged a vase of flowers on the dressing table. I expected some change in him but he was still the same Professor Spence who always looked at me when he spoke, even if he was conversing with someone else.

Nora left us alone to discuss Camilla's convulsions. He listened with his head on one side to my jumbled account of what had happened; when there was nothing more to add to the case history he stood up and began striding up and down the room as though he was addressing an audience in a lecture theatre.

'A convulsion is one of the worst experiences a mother can ever witness in her child. However, it must not be confused with an epileptic fit. It is often a reaction to a drug. . . .' And the treatment? Aspirin.

A victory for me, but I didn't want to gloat. I was far too happy with our after-dinner walk. We stayed out so late that we needed the glow worms to show us our way home in the dark.

Nora and I made a few jaunts by train and buses to look at possible houses, and when she was in a 'that will do' mood I had difficulty in persuading her that a surburban horror in Gerards Cross with a back garden running down to the railway embankment was not what we wanted although it was convenient for the shops and other boring, sensible considerations like that. Mercifully an advertisement in the *Observer* caught my eye; without any dilly-dallying we went to inspect this house on Richmond Green. I got there early and sat under a tree wishing the charming, Georgian house with the crumbling façade was the one we had come to see and not its less attractive next door neighbour which was in a better state of repair. When Erasmus arrived he told me I had mixed up the numbers – it was like the best sort of April Fool. In spite of a murky basement, a dark staircase winding its way up to five floors and a surveyor's report that would put anyone off we went ahead and bought it. We celebrated our seventh wedding anniversary by spending the day there, picnicking in the garden admiring the willow herb growing over the air-raid shelter and listening to the church bells which had started to ring.

Gwen Raverat's visit to Boswells started a chain of events which ended us up in the Aylesbury law courts. One morning, while she was half asleep in bed, the door slowly opened and the face of a land-girl appeared before disappearing without saying a word. We laughed at this story and thought no more about it until Erasmus, as a future householder, went to check on our wedding presents. They had been stored for the last seven years in tea chests in the loft beyond the attic where the land-girl slept. The tea chests were empty. All the Pyrex dishes had gone. Gwen's story became an important part of the evidence. It put the police on the right track which led to the land-girl's arrest – and the return of our wedding presents. Pyrex dishes, more Pyrex dishes, a Jensen sugar basin, a Lalique bowl, and more Pyrex dishes were on display round the court for us to identify.

Gwen was still at Boswells when the Japanese war ended. She told us that her brother Charles had had something to do with the bomb. For the moment we were grateful for that bomb which later on we would condemn. I joined in the celebrations this time. We mingled with the crowds outside Buckingham Palace and linked arms with strangers as we walked down the Mall. Afterwards I felt rather grubbily ashamed at having taken part in so much mass emotion.

I expected everything to change for the better now that peace was declared but I soon found myself engaged in my own private war. Camilla had to go on traction as part of the treatment for her Perthe's disease. I wanted to nurse her at home. A big undertaking, I knew. Erasmus agreed but he couldn't be there when I turned to the family for support and met only strong opposition.

In our new house with all those stairs, it would be impossible. And a whole year, would my health stand it? Camilla
would be so much better off in hospital. There would be lots
of other children in the ward. She would settle down quickly,
children always do, and they would have each other for company. I could visit her. Once or twice a week, no more,
because visits could be upsetting when a child had adapted to
the hospital routine.

An eminent orthopaedic surgeon in Harley Street, who had
never heard of mother love, added weight to the general con-
sensus of opinion. Day and night assistance would be needed
if I really was so mad as to want to nurse my own child at
home. And who had I got to help? Kathleen. Little use she
would be. The daft girl couldn't be relied upon to do anything
properly. She hadn't yet learned which shoe went on
which foot.

And Erasmus spending so many nights in the hospital
always on call, he needed consideration surely; he must have
peace when he came home. Nora, Aunt Helen, Joan, even
Alan had something to say. Round and round the arguments
went, arguments that only strengthened my resolve not to
weaken. Something terribly important was at stake. I must not
try to please and let myself be over-ridden as I had in the past.
It was all right to forego my choice of wedding music and
change a baby's name for the sake of a grandmother's whim,
but this was of a different category. Camilla's future, my own
integrity, a principle were being threatened. I must nurse my
own child at home, if I didn't do that I would be breaking faith
with myself. It would be a sin, a sin against the Holy Ghost for
all I knew. Right was on my side. Professor Spence too.

I wrote Professor Spence a long letter telling him what the
reaction of the family had been to my nursing Camilla at
home. He made a special journey to Boswells and pleaded my
case like the most skilful QC. He wielded statistics and quoted
examples from his latest book. He had the facts and the
figures at his fingertips of the harm hospitalisation could do to
a child. Such scientifically based arguments seemed irrefut-
able to a family who had become unusually emotional.

'Do you think he's in love with you?' Nora asked after Professor Spence had gone. No need to think very hard before
replying as I'd given the subject a lot of thought.

'Yes,' I said, 'but he'll only stay in love with me as long as I have a sick child.' As I spoke her eyes were level with mine, Usually I looked up to her when I talked but now, suddenly, she seemed to have shrunk so that we were the same size. I watched her walk across the hall with that characteristic step which on the polished floor-boards resounded, like the hooves of a brisk pony. I loved my mother-in-law.

Nora and I spent our last evening together as we had spent so many evenings in the past – sitting in front of the drawing-room fire, our knitting needles competing with the ticking clock. Our conversations, if strung together, would make a long and interesting dialogue. Many subjects had been covered, and while we skimmed and delved, feelings had inevitably been hurt. Like good boxers, we recovered in our corners, and when the gong sounded we went back into the ring ready for more.

I regretted some of the things I had said. I regretted too the opportunities lost to say things I should have said. Nora interrupted my dwelling in the past by worrying over the future.

'Will you really be able to manage Camilla on that traction?' she asked.

'Of course I will,' I assured her, 'we've designed a bed for the night and a smaller one for the day. The smaller one fits on a trolley which Kathleen is longing to push out every afternoon. We've already found a table that fits over the bed. She can draw, polish silver and iron her doll's clothes. There are lots of ways I can amuse her. I might even buy a budgie or a kitten.'

Nora smiled at my rush of enthusiasm. 'I must say, Biddy, you do rise to an occasion,' she said, and added, 'I'll never forget when I first saw you – such a pale sickly little thing. Dressed as a fairy.'

I dropped my knitting and said, very firmly,

'No Nora. I was a snowflake.'

'But I remember you quite clearly. You were all in white, dressed as a fairy.'

'I was dressed in white because I was a snowflake.' There was an edge to my voice.

'The mistaken identity obviously rankles,' she said. We looked at each other and began laughing.